ᴛʜᴇ MYSTERY ᴏꜰ
Rosa Morland

Also by Diane Fahey

THE MYSTERY OF
ROSA MORLAND

Diane Fahey

To dear Katherine,
With love,
Diane

C

Clouds of Magellan — Melbourne

© Diane Fahey 2008

First published 2008

Clouds of Magellan Publishing — www.cloudsofmagellan.net

ISBN 978-0-9802983-3-8

National Library of Australia Cataloguing-in-Publication data:

Fahey, Diane

The mystery of Rosa Morland

ISBN: 9780980298338 (pbk.)

A823.3

Cover design: Gordon Thompson

Cover image: © V&A Images/Victoria and Albert Museum, London

Distribution in Australia: www.bulldogbooks.com.au

This work was assisted by a New Work Grant from the Literature
Board of the Australia Council, the Australian Government's arts
funding and advisory body.

Australian Government

Australia **Council**
for the Arts

CONTENTS

RIVER OF LIFE, RIVER OF DEATH

AT WAVERLEY STATION

BIOGRAPHIES

THE MASKED BALL

About the Author

*

NOTE

The end of the nineteenth century was on the last day of 1900,
according to the Gregorian calendar and was celebrated on
this day.

---

*Chapter 1 of *The Secret of Bloodstone Castle*, 1900.

Separately published in *The Illustrated London News,* January, 1901.

**Chapter 1 of *Laura Osmund: A Woman of the Dales,* 1902.

Separately published in *Blackwood's Edinburgh Review,* July, 1902.

***An excerpt from *The Fawnfield Chronicles,* 1903.

Sleeping Car Plan and List of Travellers

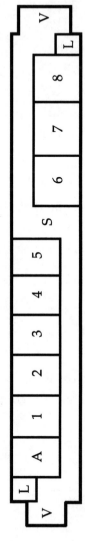

V	L
A	1	2	3	4	5	S	6	7	8	L	V

A = Attendant's Compartment; S = Smoking Saloon; L = Lavatory; V = Vestibule Entrance

OCCUPANTS

Attendant's Compartment:
A. Thomas Quinn

Single Compartments:
1. Jasper Abbott, a Clockmaker
2. Ernest Watts, a Detective Inspector
3. Florence Ellesmere, an Actress;
   and Dolores, a Scarlet Macaw
4. Alasdair Lockhart, a Naturalist
5. Eustace Maldonbury, a Baron

Double Compartments:
6. Charlotte Winter, a Lady's Companion
   Anne Morgan, a Lady's Maid
7. Elinor Pierce, an ex-Baroness
   Seamus L'Estrange, a Physician and Photographer
8. Helen and Claire Westwood,
   Mother and Daughter

AT KING'S CROSS STATION

DOLORES

The place where I began was a green dusk
with slanted spears igniting vines, toucans
with black-and-gold beaks, glasswing butterflies;
it was a borderless map over which
my flight scrolled an eccentric signature.
Mulch carpet, and chandeliers of leaves
hanging from hot blue — I played the distances
between them, my scarlet and yellow cries
filled the rainforest's dripping voice-box.
I was kidnapped, taken to live inside
a closed collective mind — among porcelain
sylphs and swains, stuffed owls, aspidistras.
The eyes of peacock feathers gleamed by altars
of heaped rubies, and died with them: transposed,
like myself, to paraphernalia.
An exiled Amazon queen, I gazed through
gilt bars, the gift of speech my only joy.
I revolved sounds like seeds in my beak, gnawed at
phrases as if they were cuttlefish bones
to be scraped into chalky hollows.
Intoning words fraught with sardonic mirth,
an eerie dread, I breached the unspoken.
Thus I became a pirate of forbidden thoughts —
to be released in Rabelaisian spurts,
raucous chunks or mind-teasing fragments.

And there were days when no words would come,
when I repined — a third-rate music-hall star,
waiting in my wings. But not tonight!
Crowds part as I'm borne across this vast stage —
in a state of thrilled prescience, my cage-cloak
of royal blue drawn back as if a curtain.
Like a retired diva craving the smell
and hush and violence of the theatre,
I dream of new, astonishing flights
above limelit sawdust...
      How fitting then
that I've been chosen to launch this tale:
instructive, diverting, or wicked? —
you, dear reader, must judge.

BEFORE MIDNIGHT

THOMAS QUINN

In boyhood, railways were my hobby.
Luckily, I kept the train set Dad gave me,
can watch it circle the parlour carpet
on Sunday afternoons with young Davey.
Last summer, Maggie and I brought him
to see the train I work on, the East Coast Sleeper.
Davey's eyes grew large as we passed by
engines of forest green, deep-sea blue.
When my train left at a quarter to nine,
his arm waved me out; I watched that
tiny red semaphore and Maggie's black hair
as we eased from King's Cross into twilight...
Six nights a week I do a sleeping car.
My job's to check in passengers, help with
luggage; later, I sort cups of tea.
A few hours' sleep snatched after midnight.
Approaching Dunbar I'm busy again
but if there's a moon I take a minute
to gaze at the North Sea — a wilderness
of shadows soundlessly heaving, falling.
Once in at Waverley, it's through the dark
to my room, sleep, an afternoon stroll
down Princes Street. Fish and chips for dinner,
a read of the newspaper.
                              Even tonight,

far from home on New Year's Eve, I enjoy
the translation from England to Scotland,
swapping that steamy glasshouse for silent hills
and hamlets, watching for comets from my cubby.

Clock maker

JASPER ABBOTT

It was time to stop. Time for my eyes
and fingers to abdicate from the mystery
sealed off from me now as I contemplate
merely the makeshift architecture of time
in rooms, town squares — clocks rewound until
they fall into an otherworldly silence.
As I shall, between one tick and the next.
Eventually. The dust settling on them
will settle on me...
                    Before that comes,
I, who tended spurred wheels gilded by light
with instruments fine as insect legs,
thistledown wire, will wind squat mantel clock
like a bank clerk. I'll polish its glass, listen:
a maker and healer of timepieces
become a diurnal key-turner.
Meanwhile, I journey to my new life —
an unhoused spirit speeding through time, black space.
Tomorrow I'll climb to an attic beneath
a great clocktower's apocalyptic chiming.
There, my pleasure will be to track the stars
with a telescope, watch them glimmer and glint
like my tray of cog-wheels and escapements
scattered on blue-black velvet.

BARON MALDONBURY

Byronic of me, but I loved her. Once.
For a year at least... Why she accepted me
I'll never understand. Not now. Should've
asked her before I left to climb Mount Gaunt
that day of grey snow, a year and one week ago.
But such a query might've brought on an attack:
that frail, resistant body changed to
a puffer fish gasping inside whalebone...
If fatal, this would have defeated
my plan for a death by remote control:
guileful, deep-laid, yet utterly risky –
the gambler in me relishes long odds...
Why, *I* could die tonight, just sitting here
smoking a cigar — a loose flake could detach,
catch in my throat, and I cough myself purple
till I'd run out of time and breath: hot ash
on my tongue, and my fifty-year-old heart
bursting like an over-heated boiler.
Well, it's fun to imagine!
                              Murder, now...
For mine, it could be standing by, puffing
like fury on a fresh cigar, while your
asthmatic beloved breathes her last —
nature doing the job for you. As above!
Some might say, though, you were implicated...

10

Better to be half-way up a mountain —
as I was when she died; half-way down,
the news reached me. Oxygen was sparse
so I could sympathise, in my fashion.
That was a year ago — the perfect crime.
And yet... often I'm harried by doubts
as to whether, in fact, I did it.
Am I her murderer? In the small hours
the question nags me like an ulcer, or a wife.
So undetectable the means I chose,
how *can* I be sure they really worked?
All evidence of intent I destroyed
on reaching home to attend her funeral —
long delayed for me. Glorious day!
I donned my widower's black, a face of woe,
and followed her bodiless coffin
to the crypt...
        I've made an ironic shrine:
a library of novels authored by her —
six books bound in red, that Elinor
didn't know I knew about. Or did she?
In those last minutes, perhaps, if she knew
that I was killing her — if I was —
she'd have known I knew of her secret life:
the colossal insult of it to me.
Because only that would explain why...
I mean, we could have gone on loathing

each other for decades — and loving it.
Thousands do... Dear me, so exhausting!
It must be time for my hourly nip.
And a peek at *Lord Rutherton's Revenge*.
(What a devious old rat he is!)
Not one by our Rosa — no indeed!

ERNEST WATTS

'Rosa!' I said. That made her stop, turn round
and look me full in the face for the first time...
We'd been discussing her bizarre plan
over tea: gold-rimmed cups, cress
sandwiches, talk of plots and counter-plots.
All the while I was dizzy with her —
silken light on her lips, her brow; those eyes,
green star-crystals; upswept auburn hair.
When she opened the door to show me out,
I, halfway across the room, said 'Rosa!'
My gaze fingered the line of red-spined books
on the shelf. 'With respect, Lady Maldonbury,
I'm not a detective for nothing.'
For an instant I thought I'd bested her.
She paused, shut the door with calm intent.
'What you speak of is pure play. This is real.'
Then she smiled — a sunburst after brief rain...
As both of us knew, she needed me.
Her white hand reached into a silver bowl,
took out a brooch, offered it to me:
a rose-image enclosed in crystal,
as if frozen under water. My palm weighed
its curved smoothness. 'I'll see what can be done.'
I coughed then disappeared; the door closed softly.

FLORENCE ELLESMERE

Applause: the fluttering of a million wings!
At my feet, coral and ivory blooms unfurled
from gold hearts as waterfalls of velvet
spilt crimsonly down, surged upwards.
Yet there were from the first, days, whole weeks
of fatigue when the pleasure of it left me.
I practised patience, gave all from nothing —
showering those rapt faces with gifts
from beggarhood. My Ariel-spirit
served while dreaming its freedom…
                                        In full flight,
my voice of gold, ebony and lava
filled that darkened space like a great ear;
unseen eyes met each smouldering glance.
Even as a betrayed wife, letter
in hand, pacing the confines of a drawing room,
or a captive Queen, paraded in
the marketplace, I moved like a swan.
Then — arrived at the middle years,
the height of my powers — I must play
strumpet, murderess, bitter scold:
all the sordid trivia of men's fears, desires.
So that I became a cliff buffeted
by hostile waves, eaten by the sea…
Enough! I have silenced that sea, left that

precipice curving towards emptiness.
Soon I'll sit between burgundy drapes
in a house on Edinburgh's quietest,
most hidden street. Calmly, I'll set the stage
for glimpsing limelit shards of the future.
The cards will confirm what eyes, stance,
rhythm of breath and upturned hands tell me.
But I will take no dictation from the dead,
nor ever invoke them. Let them sleep,
or speak through dreams. My gift is to grasp
what's just beyond reach — as if gazing from
half-closed eyes at a receding vision…
In the theatre I was adept at
waiting wordless while others declaimed,
ranted — with no hint of stage business
I kept all eyes upon me. So here,
I'll be in charge of each performance:
Life's bounty and Fate's mercy must do the rest…
I'll know what can be said and not said;
what will stall harm, turn from obsession,
dispel vain hopes. I'll know. It's like tasting
a line's flavour before you say it.
I've spent my lifetime working on that.

ALASDAIR LOCKHART

[handwritten annotation: Bird life → Charlotte Winter]

Can you fall in love with a voice?
But first I glimpsed her boarding the train:
a shimmering, cloud-bright vision — face veiled,
her throat chokered by a scarf, the glint
of pearl earrings; long velvet coat, dove-grey.
(Her maid followed, prosaic in dour blue;
upon her hat, a bird nested in green net;
black kid gloves, a black brolly. Turning,
she met my glance with sceptical grey eyes.)
I crushed my first infatuation for
that taut profile, that elusive form —
but now, ensconced in the Smoking Lounge,
I find myself — reluctantly, of course —
catching words from the wall's other side.
Mistress and maid chatting — the latter with
a Welsh inflection; the first, angel-voiced.
They seem to be speaking of a novel:
false identities, a masked ball, fat gulls,
spoilt belles, and a boldly handsome Spaniard.
Not autobiography, I think!
Hearing their secrecy-tinged laughter
feels yet more thrilling, and more intrusive…
But with these ears so finely tuned to birds
in the wild — able to trace an owl parrot
fossicking through leaves on a moonless night —

16

how can I help tracking this *rara avis*?
She has a spouse, no doubt, and lives behind
tall windows, on some vast estate...
Surely I'd not want to be the lover
in that novel they're discussing, would I?
Oh, I've been too long away — haunted
by calls and flutterings, dawn hymns of praise.
My senses are preternaturally sharp.
I must dull them, shut out what I can't have,
fend off dreams of a woman — luminous,
nonpareil — with a voice I would die for.

CHARLOTTE WINTER

As a governess, for many years
I acted insignificance, mindless
service, all the colourless virtues.
Now I am a rich woman's keeper,
acting conversational echo,
unadorned foil to florid beauty — blessed with
a reassuring lack of every talent
my lady thinks she can lay claim to.
Thus I draw in secret, never sing.
Yet since my lady's a fantasist,
my days are somewhat livelier now.
I must read aloud novels of sensation
full of family madness and cursed castles,
with fat cuckolds, lovers in midnight gardens —
and a sinning, voluptuous heroine...
I read in an unconsenting voice
dull as clay, that *she* thinks is mine.
But it's my voice for *her*. And since my lady
believes her fantasies, and lives them,
I'm also a bearer of covert letters,
an abashed sentinel of trysts and transports —
vows, rows, operatic displays.
Things I wish not to hear she tells me:
that *he* — Rodrigo, her current amour —
is 'a swashbuckling pirate with *such*

a busy sword!' I ask the name of his ship.
('The Ship of Fools', so *I* think.) She gulps her tea
and gurgles with sly laughter at the fire-screen,
rife with scenes of rural ravishment:
lutes under leaves, pert smiles, spilt wine,
frothy petticoats ... stale crusts, lost shoes.
I'd feel sorry for her portly lord
had he not poked at me with hot eyes, hot words,
hot hands — though naught else: near-powerless
as I was, he knew my rage when I
showed it, fierce as a visitation of serpents!
Now he thinks I'm the Medusa herself,
which suits me well...
                         Surprising that he,
who plays the game himself, is blind to *her* game.
The present plot is her masterpiece:
she has created a second self.
At this moment she sits opposite me —
a study in grey-garbed propriety.
And at this same moment she whirls and flirts
beneath waterfalls of crystal at
Lady De Vere McClintock's Grand Masked Ball
in Edinburgh — having left London
in disguise at dawn. Eyes brimming with intrigue,
rouge on puffy cheeks, she'll be waiting
at Waverley to resume her role.
Then we'll leave, she and I, in the carriage

he will have sent — the Bloated One, back at
his crumbling pile, Rumbervie Castle.
Meanwhile I sit, reviving my wilted
French by reading of Madame Bovary.
But I'm bored with her boredom! How galling
to be caught up in the double life
of another while lacking a true life of my own.
I yearn for sleep but will stay wakeful
to mark this end-of-an-epoch moment.
I feel a hundred years old myself:
there can be no surprises for me now.
On the shelf, the wren nested in my hat
looks plumply pleased — as if sitting on
an egg. Oh, those bright brown eyes... of glass!
Oh, the hours, the days, the centuries!

ANNE MORGAN

Being put in a false position is
no news to me. I wear a dress grander,
needless to say, than any I've ever
dreamed of, but filled with another woman's
smell that I do not want near me. In vain
I've tried to mask that mix of powder, priceless
perfume and sweat with lavender water.
At least I'm in my own stays — but pulled tighter
than I'm used to: when I undress there'll be
weals down my ribs… Still, it pleases me
to look the perfect copy of my lady.
Though I've been a scraper and bower before
heaped grates and children's muddy shoes, I,
being young, stand straighter than her.
It's made me ever so nervous — fearing
I'd forget myself and speak, or shout
in fright, ruin everything! At King's Cross,
the way ordinary folk like me stared —
or looked away, or down. I hated it.
Yet behind that veil I felt… invisible!
I stepped up first into the sleeping car,
as we'd agreed, then stood, my lips pressed shut,
while Charlotte spoke with the attendant.
Now, safe in our compartment, I'm just
dying to talk! First though, I'll settle down,

take out my book: *Lady Audley's Secret*.
It's torn and old and creepy — but I like it!
No doubt *she's* the murderer: her husband's
down that unused well in the garden, I'll bet.
Poor chap, arriving home from Australia
with his hard-earned fortune — what a waste!
She'll never get away with it; or will she?
I've brought treats for this special midnight:
we servants have ways of hiving off
portions of ham and cake — sherry, too!
I plan to be as tipsy as a lark
when the new century starts up. Ta Ra!
Won't Charlotte be surprised by the feast!
I plan to beat her later at rummy.
(I notice she reads more slowly than me.)
Oh, let me not think of tomorrow!
Waiting in the cold at Waverley
for the train to London, then on to Wales:
all of New Year's Day to reach my real home —
for *such* a short visit! At least I'll be
in my own clothes, at leisure to think
my own thoughts as we speed past snowfields
lit by pearl skies… That I will enjoy!
And whatever's left of this cake.

SEAMUS L'ESTRANGE
Spirit Photographer

Not for me the charades of revenants:
women with hypnotic eyes, robed in
lurid drapery — like nothing so much
as animated stone effigies;
nor a dead child, dressed in Sunday best,
grafted back onto parents fixed by grief's
dissolving stare — an uncanny foetus
anchored near head or womb.
                              Once, though,
in a derelict house, as I photographed
a stairway leading nowhere, midwinter
noon bloomed from an unseen source, and —
the cloud of dust I'd stirred up, was it? —
a glimmering shroud hung in icy air;
I yearned to walk through those ghostly steps.
Thereafter I sought light-effects
that fused the unearthly with the human —
accidental poltergeists of brilliance:
a cypress avenue, corridored by summer,
to which a blown mist brought metamorphoses;
candlelit rooms of cigarette-fuelled talk;
a forgotten kettle boiling into
sunlight — all yielded chimerical
glimpses, my lens positioned itself,

the shutter guillotined illusion.
I saw, where rock sliced a waterfall,
figures dancing above white tumult;
an avalanche rolled ice into sea-foam
alive with the unborn, the unretrieved.
Stranded by storm, I watched moon-hazed drops
slide down windowed darkness — as if they would
make of absence, a continuous presence:
my gaze plumbed fathomless transparency.
At this moment, I sit staring at light
filtered by my sealed eyelids: jet and gold
mingling, glass shadows wreathed inside
a mandorla, a mural on a great dome
pulsing with my invisible blood.

HELEN WESTWOOD

[handwritten annotations: P - 125 / married George Framer, a rotter]

Where do you go when you cannot return
to the place where you've belonged? The marks
he scored across my body — once only,
in that cold onslaught — made the marks
across my soul palpable, gave them
a form; the unsealed skin I bathed and bound
in linen, healed to a scarred memory.
With profligate malice he dealt me
a dead hand, as if all the cards were his.
Now I have gone. He'll sit at a bare table.
Only the mirror will so intimately
read the burst veins and bulging eyes of his wrath:
his need to disestablish, over and over,
life's simple truth.
                    I have plucked my daughter
from his intemperate love. *Forever.*
Her six-year-old eyelids cover pearl
and lapis lazuli fit to match
the sky-gleam of any river or sea on earth.
In this small room propelled by fire and steam
we'll reach Edinburgh before dawn.
Journeying west, we will choose new names,
like talismans, for ourselves as fresh light strikes
crag and loch. At Stranraer, a steamship.
Blanched, shaking with fatigue, we'll step out

onto Ireland. There, more untraceable
journeys between two lives, two centuries —
till we arrive at a place of refuge
and beginning: time's virtue sifting
through all our days.
                    My keepsakes I've sold
to effect this stylish, disguised leaving.
Together we'll fashion new memories,
find new keepsakes.
                    Claire and I lie still:
effigies about to wake.

THE DISAPPEARING CATS

'The Disappearing Cats'

by Rosa Morland *— sensitive*

A cold day was about to turn into a bitter night. The long tree shadows across the clearing near the forest's edge were losing shape, merging in the general dimness. Thick dew covered rippling grasses.

Moira O'Merton stood in the doorway of her cottage, her eyes anxiously searching the clearing, the gaps in the trees beyond. When a figure materialised on the track leading from the woods, anxiety turned to fear — an emotion she seldom felt, being so used to living alone out here, a good mile from the village of Netherby. But her nerves were utterly on edge.

Draped in darkness, the man was walking directly towards her. When he was close enough to see clearly, her body relaxed, her breath softened. It was Constable Browne — 'Whistling Browne' as he was called by the villagers because of his habit of imitating the calls of birds while walking in the woods.

He stopped outside the gate and removed his cap.

'Those Celsianas — magic, that's what I call 'em!'

In his shyness, he always paid tribute to one of her rosebushes before addressing her; it was his way.

'Constable Browne! Good-evening to you.'

'Good-evening, Moira. A cold one, eh?'

She walked down the path to join him.

'Any news of the missing cats? Now my Tabitha's gone — I haven't seen her since yesterday. I'm so worried.'

'Oh dear, that's sad news... Well, six cats have now vanished from Netherby. There's the Wilkins family's Blackie, Dr Grieve's Dusk, Tom Trimble's Scrumpy, Miss Fairley's Donna (she's got Bella locked inside), Professor Smurthwaite's Bastet — always a mouthful, that one — and...'

Seeing her pained expression, he stopped.

'There seems no end in sight.' Moira's eyes were again searching the clearing.

'Yes, it's all very distressing. I've got my theories. But the trouble is, I can't see any sense in it.'

'A person disturbed in their mind, perhaps?'

'You'd think so. Or it could be Black Magic — you know, sacri...?' He went on quickly. 'Of course the Egyptians used to mummify cats in the tens of thousands...' A pause; he laughed desperately. 'But Ancient Egypt was such a long time ago!' Then, as if inspired, he beamed: 'Well, it might be someone with an overwhelming *love* of cats... with a big house... and a lot of money. Sardines laid on! It's also possible that...'

He was starting to drift into vagueness.

Moira said, 'Have you noticed anyone acting strangely?'

'No more than usual.' He gave an absent-minded laugh.

'What about signs of disturbed earth — seen any on your walks?'

Constable Browne tugged his brown moustache.

'A good thought. I'll keep an eye out... Yes, it's wise to be realistic. Let's not give up hope, though!' He smiled cheerfully, coughed, fell silent.

The conversation had petered out. Aware of his extreme thinness, Moira was tempted to invite him in for tea, but worried he might take it as encouragement. Especially as he was now gazing at her with that warm, dreamy expression on his face...

'Well,' she said gently, 'I suppose I'll go in and give Moonshade her dinner. She's waiting by the fire.'

Constable Browne's eyes blazed momentarily, as if looking deep into the flames of a hearth.

'Yes, the best place for her. Till I sort this out.'

'Keep well now, Ernest. God bless.'

He took a step back and made a slight bow.

'My, but those Portland roses are splendid, glowing in the dusk.'

Then, putting the cap known as his 'whistling cap' back on, he said, 'Goodnight, Moira,' and went on his way.

Moira spent the evening by her hearth, thinking. In only three days, seven cats had disappeared. They had not been individually chosen, she supposed, but taken randomly, because they happened to be out and about under the moon. Yet it seemed there was some larger design at work.

Was a stranger the culprit? Or was it someone from the village? If so, who? And why? Would such a person be driven by spite? Or secret madness? The faces of the villagers passed before her mind's eye. All seemed incapable of this particular crime.

But, if any witchcraft were suspected, she would be the first to be accused — because she grew healing herbs, and lived outside the ambit of village life. Moira had seen passing villagers spying on her garden — in search of poison-bearing plants, no doubt! But it was all innocent herbs: borage, angelica, mullein, feverfew and St John's Wort, along with her potatoes and cress, and beloved rose-trees. She knew that if she was to stop blame falling upon herself for the disappearances, the real culprit must be found.

At eleven o'clock, Moira put on her brown cloak and set out for Netherby. There was a full moon — keeping her eyes wide open, she might come upon some clue… She crossed the bridge leading into the village then slowed her pace.

Dogs barked. The windows of the houses along the main street showed faint candlelight, or were dark. A few brave cats roamed abroad. Eventually she reached the church with its graveyard and, going to the graves of her mother and grandmother, sat down between them. Over fifty years before, during the time of the Great Famine, Rose O'Merton had come from Ireland, newly widowed and soon to give birth to her only child: Moira's mother, Kathleen.

Moira looked up at the stars, as she and her mother had often done together, searching for guidance. Midnight must be near... Then she heard, not far away, a whining creak. The door of the crypt! She crept past gravestones, over soft or hard earth, then stood beside the great yew with its tip piercing the luminous silver-white disc above. From there she could see a light inside the vault where many generations of the Mintingworth family had been buried in raised stone tombs.

Keeping to the shadows, Moira drew closer to the steps leading down to the iron-barred door — through which she glimpsed a figure stooped over one of the tombs. Was it Lord Mintingworth himself? Yes. Lamplight flickered over his reddish skin, black brows and moustache. He was working swiftly, with a stroking motion, above something she could not see. Moira focused her eyes intently and saw, with a horrified gasp, a cat lying on the stone. Dead. He was combing and combing its fur, slowly turning that limp body. From time to time, his hand moved from the cat — it was a tabby — to an open jewel-box. Suddenly she knew the cat was Tabitha!

Moira broke away from her concealed position and ran through the graveyard, weeping. Fear and horror coursed through her blood, but grief was uppermost. In her distraught state she stumbled, tripping over a hump of earth and falling into a deep, chill darkness.

A blinding thud. Moments, or minutes, lost... Then full awareness returned. Her head had knocked against something sharp — a stone, it must be. A rectangle of night sky loomed above her: she was lying in an open grave! (No doubt the one dug for old Mr Partridge, who had collapsed and died on Friday.) Physical pain was now added to grief. Were any of her bones broken? She felt them crushed together in a foretaste of death's intimacy. What could she do but lie still, gathering her wits and strength? As she regained her breath, Moira waited, listened.

She heard the wind in the yew tree, a raven's jagged cry. The hinges of the crypt door creaked again... Footsteps coming closer; a discordant tune being sung. Then a heavy sack thumped down onto her chest, followed by a thick rain of earth, covering both her and ... what could it be but poor, dead Tabitha? Was she about to be buried alive?

The clods stopped falling. The footsteps went away. She pushed off the blanket of earth, rose, and climbed with difficulty out of the grave — first placing the sack containing Tabitha's body up on its edge. Her journey back through the village was, in contrast to her earlier walk, an agonising one. As Moira neared home, she saw Moonshade waiting in the window. Beneath the lilac tree, she buried her beloved Tabitha that night, ashen moonlight covering the freshly-dug earth.

Once inside her cottage, she lit candles and set a new fire. Taking a small engraved box from a niche above the mantelpiece, she lifted its lid and peered at the crystalline dust inside — like a rainbow ground into particles. As soon as the flames on the hearth began to leap, she threw a handful of the powder — composed of crushed, dried rose petals — onto the flames. The dust exploded into myriad flashing colours. This was a ritual her mother had taught her. Moira contemplated the images she saw above the flames and knew what she must do.

Tomorrow she would take herbs to the kitchen at Bloodstone Castle, and while there find a way of speaking to the mistress, Lady Violet Mintingworth. This would be difficult as she lived surrounded by veils and curtains in an enclosed part of the house where silence reigned. Few people, and no animals, could go there. Her strange illness was believed to have begun soon after her marriage, and was blamed on her pet cat, White Midnight — a gift from her husband, Eustace.

Moira would find a way to tell Violet of what she believed was a great danger approaching her. Indeed, it might already be too late... She prayed it would not be, and went to rest on her bed. Before dawn, a dream of a hidden passageway through a dusty labyrinth came to her. If this was a sign of a secret route hidden in that vast, decaying castle, she would find it.

AFTER MIDNIGHT

THOMAS QUINN

Porter

There's been trouble in the past — one lady
dead of heart failure, and a colonel who
suffered a stroke: we stopped the train at Selby
where he was taken post-haste to a doctor.
You do what you can in such situations.
Over time I've learnt to expect surprises...
Tonight, when Lockhart came to my door,
I was somewhat bright-eyed — having seen
the new century in with a ritual glass.
Said he'd heard noises after Doncaster
(we'd left there at 12.20) — a thump,
something breaking, in the next compartment.
(Number 5 — Lord Maldonbury.)

The murder?

It was half twelve... No answer to my knock.
I tried the door — unlocked; no one there!
The blind was up, the window down — strong rain
slanting in through blackness. I turned the light on.
A suitcase lay open on the seat —
clothes in a jumble, a gash of wet crimson
across them: the blood-trail led to the sill.
On the floor, a bottle without its neck;
whisky fumes hit despite the rushing air.
On the rack, a top hat and fawn overcoat...
Suicide was what I feared — a mad,
drunken suicide. Perhaps a botched job:

he could be sprawled on some embankment,
full of broken bones...
                              At that point
I remembered the policeman on board.
(His name, heading my list, had caught my eye.
As he'd approached the car I knew him
straight off — that closed-in, vigilant look...
Detective Inspector Ernest Watts.)
I went to raise him. He was awake, still dressed.
Arrived at the scene, he looked shattered,
his face cucumber-white. Surprising,
I thought, in one seasoned to violence.
Besides, it's not as if there was a body!
Just a macabre absence... Watts seemed at a loss
then rallied, made a search, asked me about
the occupant — whose name he already knew.
We left, sealing in that ghastly tableau...
Blood, the smell of whisky, an open window.

ALASDAIR LOCKHART

My first day back in Britain marked by a death...
While I was sitting here after midnight,
still caught in the toils of infatuation,
conjuring her veiled profile, her veiled voice,
I was but a wall away from mayhem.
I'd felt ashamed, there in the Smoking Lounge
next to *her* compartment, listening to words
nebulous as the smoke rising before me.
Then that stifled laughter — so alluringly
secretive... It seemed indecent to linger.
Back here by eleven. At midnight
I heard voices — heated ones this time —
through the wall. A man uttering threats;
a long pause; more threats; then a woman's voice —
impassioned, terse...

       (The occupant I'd seen:
a manicured specimen, with moustache
and over-long hair dyed black, in defiance
of lined, pouched skin. He'd winced at my greeting.)
Soon a second man's voice joined the fray —
but so reined in, I could hardly hear it.
The door slammed with a curse!

                Miles of silence
then the thud, the splintering crash...
My knock went unanswered; I called Tom Quinn.

41

The door opened on nightmare. Rain blew in,
soaking blood-stained clothes, the velvet seat.
We stared in shock… Quinn said he'd inform
a police detective who was on board.
Now, my mind has begun to sift details
as if I were a detective myself.
(So I am, in my chosen profession.)
That rake in his superbly tailored coat,
with his aquiline nose, flared nostrils,
the silver ring with a carbuncular flash,
and those pale blue eyes lacquered with contempt —
he'd be a hard man to outwit, or do in.
He looked capable of anything;
a bad enemy, I'd say. What's going on
in that mind of his now — if he still has one?

ERNEST WATTS

Mostly I'm a silent man — self-erasing,
it would seem. But I've a non-conformist streak:
witness my presence on this train tonight.
I'm here at the behest of Elinor Pierce
who promised to draw a confession
of attempted murder from her husband:
(jubilant widower for a year).
Her evidence, tenuous as it was,
intrigued me, but could not prevail
in court against so powerful a man.
I'd agreed to help, unofficially:
to position us near Lord Maldonbury
on the train she knew he'd take to Scotland
on New Year's Eve (his custom, no one knows why,
for all of twenty years — save the last);
to listen, unseen, to their exchange;
and prevent violence against her.
Was she, in asking so much, presuming
upon my obsession with her? Perhaps.
But then, I wanted to be presumed upon…
The confrontation began well — a ghost
always has the advantage of surprise.
Her words hung in the air. 'Remember me?'
Something caught in his throat: choking sounds
from a gargoyle mouth, a volley of coughs,

then oaths fit to fill a barrack-room.
Countering his attack, Rosa plucked from
her coat, a novel, *The Secret of Bloodstone Castle*
(given into her hands the day before),
and thrust it into his hands, opened at
Chapter One — not what you'd call proof,
though the tale was told clearly enough.
Ice-blue eyes swept page after page
till he ripped the book apart and flung it
at her, vowing to finish his work.
He taloned her wrist, moved to shut the door.
My right foot materialised in the doorway.
I grabbed Elinor's left arm — announced
myself — put him on notice of charges.
He lunged, forced us outside, slammed the door:
the lock clicked; sounds of furious movement.
What to do now? Waiting him out seemed
my only choice — waiting me out, his...
I took Elinor to her companion,
glad for the first time of his presence — needed,
she had assured me, in case of ill health...
L'Estrange revived her with the inhaler
then held her as she sat, reclaiming breath.
I left to write notes, reach self-command.
In the midst of this drama, I could not
but feel used by Elinor: to help trap
her would-be murderer; ensure a safe

return to the lover I so envied.
Hard enough. But now, a darker twist!
Murder, maybe... or suicide. Escape? —
not from this swift train. If murder, by whom?
I saw the shadowed eyes of Doctor L'Estrange,
and Elinor's suffering, defiant eyes.
A cornucopia of motives there...
And I saw myself waiting outside that door —
just half an hour before discovering
Lord Maldonbury was gone.
                                    I'd no choice now
but to start an investigation; later,
my name might appear on the list of suspects.
(Was I seen in the corridor at midnight,
or my voice overheard in that mêlée?)
So: should Elinor and I try to
protect ourselves by inventing a story?
No doubt she'd relish the challenge — weaving
words that would beggar belief, turn black
into white.
                    But my small dignity
lies in seeking the truth — even though
seemingly implicated myself;
even if it should mean her death, or mine.
Or L'Estrange's... (Such a strongly-built man —
well able to subdue the Maldonburys
of this world?)

I'll interview each person
in this car — starting with Elinor Pierce.
To get it over with. Then *him* — her chosen
consort, travelling as her husband.
I have till dawn to piece it together.

ELINOR PIERCE

A knock. Seamus rose and opened the door.
Ernest Watts stood there: his sad face
pinched with suspicion, those brown eyes stern,
unflickering. He stepped in and told us:
Lord Maldonbury had gone missing...
Some miles out from Doncaster, the last stop,
there'd been a loud crash in his compartment.
When called to investigate, Watts found:
a pile of blood-stained clothes on his suitcase,
broken glass and a smashed whisky bottle
down on the floor; thick rain was blowing in.
Watts paused, grew paler still, gathered himself.
At the very least he's badly wounded,
but could be dead. If so, it may be murder.
I felt appalled — then so dizzy with relief
I almost swooned.
                    Watts' tone of voice hardened.
'I must ask, Miss Pierce, if you have left
this compartment since... five past midnight.'
'No. When you went I took some brandy —
still distraught after the assault. I rested.
Doctor L'Estrange bandaged my wrist. Soon,
my breathing calmed.'
                    Watts' gaze shifted. 'And you, sir.
In that time did you leave the compartment?'

Elinor's r Seamus' intrigue

'Yes. To get some water for Elinor.

It must've been ten past twelve. I hurried back.'

Watts fingered the blank page of his notebook.

'How would you describe your relations

with Lord Maldonbury?' As intended,

a prickly silence. 'I knew him as a patient;

and socially. But we were not friends.'

The notebook snapped shut. 'I'll speak to you again

at journey's end. By then, things may be clearer.'

He bowed with a despairing look; was gone.

Seamus and I exchanged glances. For us,

the situation was perilous. And Watts?

He must have felt compromised — trapped in

a labyrinth of my devising.

I'd never intended that. Had I?

JASPER ABBOTT

Called from deep sleep to this nightmare: the solemn,
brown-moustached face of a policeman
holding me to account. I stood dishevelled
before him, seeing, in my mind's eye,
the object beneath my pillow — placed there
with such a sense of safety! For this threat
of exposure I was unprepared: having
committed, so I thought, the perfect crime —
undetectable because unknowable…
I, Jasper Abbott, made a timepiece
shaped like a phoenix during my life as
a clockmaker — purloining from the rich,
jewel-shards, flakes of beaten gold, so I'd have,
at the end, something precious of my own:
a sparkling shrine commemorating
my service to time, and the beautiful…
Little by little, over forty years:
you'd hardly call it theft.
                              His gaze held mine.
Where was I between midnight and now?
(Nowhere but in that vat of oblivion,
sleep — my head above my rubied prize
waiting to be dreamed…
                              When the carved hands met
on that mother-of-pearl breast, I swaddled

the bird in flame-bright silk and buried it
under my pillowed head — ready to die to
the past, begin my flight towards the future.)
I'm stuttering as I answer, my face
is blank with concealed fright. But he's satisfied —
thinking, perhaps, I'm half-asleep, dream-dazed.
And his questions do not concern a phoenix
with emerald eyes, and ebony wings
inlaid with gold, ivory. *Tempus fugit...*   *Dolores*
He shuts his notebook. I close the door.

FLORENCE ELLESMERE

The police inspector stood in the doorway:
small, nondescript — yet he carried the part.
First, an admission: he knew of my fame,
was an admirer; had seen, many times,
The Pearl Necklace... Then, with a grave look,
he spoke of a passenger gone missing:
Signs of foul play — murder was on the cards,
so he believed... Perhaps I'd heard of the man
in question — his name, famous in its way, is...
(But I'd guessed already, having glimpsed him
early that night: if anyone had been
murdered on this train, it must surely be...)
Lord Eustace Maldonbury?
                'I know of him,
yes; we've never met.' (And I recalled,
years before, a spray of blood-red roses,
a note like a thorn, requesting my presence
at a supper. I tore the note to bits,
confettied the roses, sent them straight back.)
During the last hour, had I seen or heard
anything... strange... or unusual?
'It was like this. I had my door open,
hoping to catch some passerby for a chat —
a toast to the New Year, the New Century.
Yet even on this night, no one about.

(Though I'd swear I saw you, Inspector,
hovering in the corridor, near twelve?)
It was silent as a robbed grave at midnight;
soon after, I heard sounds — a celebration,
I assumed. Ten or so minutes later
a man in a tweed suit strode past, returned
with a pitcher of water. At twelve thirty
a red-haired man rushed by — the attendant
followed him back; I saw them enter
the last single compartment. Intrigued,
I went to take a peek... A blast of chill air
as from a crypt — glass shards — blood and rain
soaking ransacked clothes, the plush seat. Ghastly!
— though it did remind me of a stage set.'
The detective's eyes were busy in his face.
'So, Inspector...' (I wanted to know more.)
But, with the ghost of a smile, he thanked me,
made a slight bow then exited left.
I took out brandy, the cache of birdseed:
now Dolores and I could set to work
on the case... We reviewed the latest scandal
involving Lord M. He'd stolen sapphires
from Celia, Duchess of Wigforth, who —
smitten — had invited him to dinners,
weekend parties: until he'd had his way
with her assets.
                    The Duke had forced a duel,

was shot ignobly in the thigh: the Baron
yawned, lit a cigar, strolled from the dawn field.
Yes, many a cuckolded Peer had cause
to want him gone! And with his debts and black moods,
there must have been times when...
                              Dolores' gaze
answered mine — she knew my thoughts exactly.
I shuffled the cards, set down a spread.
      The Knave of Swords crossed by The Queen of Cups.
      The Hanged Man. The Fool and The Star. The Lovers.
'Embroiled scenarios; lifelines crossing...
A phantasmagoric death followed by
shocks, reversals. Then the turning point comes,
new journeys begin — with new hazards,
of course; more unnerving surprises...'
My head was giddy with flickering scenes.
'Now to *us*, Dolores.' Her green eyes sparkled.
'I see a room with sepia shadows;
candle flames slant in an eerie wind.
Near the window, your cage, framed by ferns.
On the table, a globe lit from within
by comets and stars, words like burning flowers.
An unknown name writes itself, dissolves.
And what do we know? What, really, do we...'
With tranced eyes, Dolores danced over
the calm-faced cards; stopped; picked one up
in her beak: my hands accepted it.

CHARLOTTE WINTER

Most alarming! — that knocking, muted at first
then loud. Anne and I stared at each other.
She wrapped the scarf round her neck, but there was
no camouflaging her wine-flushed cheeks.
I brushed the crumbs away, hid what was left
of the food: within the space of thirty seconds
we arranged ourselves. As I unlocked the door,
Anne coughed loudly, her fist held to her mouth.
I saw a man with nut-brown eyes and moustache.
He was a police detective, he told us,
There'd been an incident on the train.
Just a few questions, if we didn't mind.
Once more, Anne was shaken by rasping coughs.
I touched her arm, a stricken look on my face.
We'd not moved since boarding... but for visits
down the corridor... before eleven.
His gaze swept the compartment, taking in
our shoes, our clothing, our faces, our eyes.
Exactly what could he detect from those clues?
That we were women? He thanked us and left —
upon which we agreed that Anne's breathless
performance and my quick lies had carried
the day. But we were a trifle nervous,
with strong reasons to hope this was the end
of the matter: whatever the matter was.

HELEN WESTWOOD

This is my nightmare:
He shadows me,
always. I cannot turn my head, yet know
that when I move my body, he moves his.
In bed, inches from my back, he lies curved
in foetal mimicry. Still my neck stays
fixed — so I never see him, face him.
I try to sever his image from me
as if breaking ice from a ship's hull —
ice that floats into white distance
until it joins with some frozen sea.
Now I'm running over that sea, knowing
he's somewhere beneath, carving a lesion
as jagged as his smile.
The ice splits; I fall.
My ears thud and crackle as they freeze;
a pounding like thunder...

I hear train-wheels,
a fist on wood. The line sealing my eyelids
melts: I wake with sweat pooling under
my left breast, as if it were heart's blood.
I reach to enfold Claire, safely asleep,
her fairytale hair sheened like sunlit snow.
We will help each other down from the tower,
flee the wolf with his house of poisoned bread...

I rush from the forest. Push and push
the ice away. I rise, smooth down my hair.
Breathing slowly, I open the door.

SEAMUS L'ESTRANGE

1

A secret room, a secret life... Each dusk,
the last patient seen to the surgery door,
my stethoscope hanging unwarmed by flesh
caging a thud regular as rhymed verse,
or stalled by a rogue iamb — each dusk
I sealed out those cheery, brave or fearful
faces, sealed in the smells of formaldehyde
and human sweat. I descended to
the smells of hypo and developer inside
my dark room in the cellar, transformed myself
from healer to aproned alchemist.
They hung there — negatives of passionate
light I'd been vouchsafed glimpses of...
On that night, the face of Elinor Pierce
emerged from blankness, rose dripping between
my trembling hands: her skin blanched, her cheekbones
highlighting dark half-moons beneath her eyes
(those pupils black-bright, burning; irises
grey as a winter sea). Her expression
air-starved, caught between appetite for life
and its denial. Her mouth, vulnerable.
Yet, underpinning all, an intent
composure, in despite of grave duress.

2
A cloaked figure walked, ran, staggered
into the sun's great disc, stood haloed by it
then with arched back, a hand clutched to her throat —
the other hand gesturing wildly,
unknowingly, to where I watched — she fell
headlong through that hoop of orange flame.
Sun began to elide with sea as I
sped towards the cliffs, feeling her breath gasping
inside mine, my throat a closing channel,
my body propelled onwards to the brink.
I looked down past tiered limestone: a swirl,
dark as her cloak, on sharp rocks; seaweed hair
billowing... I made my descent swiftly
in the last light, stones flew from each foothold
till I reached the jutting lip of a cave.
She lay, half-conscious, her body jack-knifed.
That was the night when, after she had
recovered, I took her photograph.

3
I was her physician, had climbed the steps
to her chamber many times, sat poised
in ambiguous intimacy...
Since her husband had been away, there'd been
more frequent calls — some late at night, her maid
sent to my door: most attacks came when

she'd retired to that blue-canopied bed.
Would she torment me beyond my limit?
Yet it seemed something else was at work,
insidiously... Indeed, it was as if
she sensed my love, held doubly back from me.
I read a new fear in her eyes, a final
resistance against an unknown foe
as her nerve fought its weakening. I urged
a change of scene, more rest, aware she lived
in that sea air without serenity;
like one who, haunted, would beard her own ghosts.
Or someone else's...
                              Then that death-night.
As her breath returned, as hope returned,
I cradled her as I would a child.
She roused herself, emerged to climb the cliff
under a cloud-eclipsed full moon; sea spray,
gull cries, no trace of colour left in the sky.
Her hands gripped broken roots, outcrops of rock.
At the top — mysteriously, to me —
she tore the hem of her skirt on thorns, fluttered
a cream handkerchief over the edge.
Wordless, we walked across the heath towards
my house, her arm in mine. There could be
no further closeness than this between us.
But our spirits were companioned now,
joined in mutual knowledge, sea-changed.

4

'No one could've seen me come here,' she said.
'I can't return to that house. I'll die there.
But if I escape tonight, now,
he'll believe me dead. That's what he wants.
Back at the house, they'll think I've had a turn,
collapsed somewhere. Soon they'll raise the alarm.
You may be called for.' Still I said nothing.
Her fingers touched my sleeve. 'I ask this.
Prepare your trap as if setting out
to visit a patient. I'll lie concealed
on the floor until we're clear of this place.
Head for Brighton Station. I'll travel
third class to London with my scarf veiling
my face, my hood drawn up. Like a spy!
A small loan from you would tide me over:
I've got money set by.
                        I will invent
a new life, a new self... This is the only way.'
In the vestibule, before we left,
I watched as lamplight bathed her eyes, grazed cheek
and those hands that had clung on for dear life.
She gave back my look, smiled her secret smile.
'A fallen woman, truly,' I said softly.

5

Chameleon woman… When next we met,
the abrasions were healed. Four weeks had passed.
She had installed herself at Bath, living
tucked away in drably elegant rooms:
as became a woman with a past — or should I say,
without one? Her eyes' deep-sea light
pierced me. After a fervent greeting
we circled each other in polite words.
A stalemate — a further plot to be resolved.
But how? *Her health was fully restored,* she said:
there'd been no more seizures… 'And you, Seamus?'
My answer was brief. She smiled. 'Let's have tea now.'

6

'This handkerchief!' It was linen, lace-edged.
Elinor placed it in my hands. 'Well?'
I peered at four joined squares. 'There's a fine dust
of something like salt and pepper, along one crease.'
'Yes?' 'And this short hair — a cat's hair, perhaps?'
'So how did it get there?' I said nothing.
'Surely that's *his* doing. This handkerchief
was in my skirt pocket the day I fell.
I'd used another, from my cloak, before
my seizure on the cliff — that was the one
I dropped after I'd climbed back up.' 'And?'
'Can't you guess why he would tamper with this?'

I walked to the window's sharper light.
'As you well know, I'm allergic to cats.
Oh, I can see his mind at work in this!
He must have put such cat-combings inside
all my handkerchiefs and each pillowcase:
hence those night seizures after he left.
Even the inhaler made me worse.'
'I collected that the next day. The police
asked my opinion, took me to the house.
"Could it be suicide?" "I believe not."
I then spoke of the pattern of your attacks,
how they'd increased, said a seizure while
on the cliff top could have caused a fall.
They made a search, found the threads from your skirt,
the dropped handkerchief, presumed a drowning.
I took the inhaler — "to pass on to
a needy patient". It's there in my black bag.'
'So we can analyse what's inside it —
use it as evidence?' 'If you're right, yes.'

7

Breathing the rose light of sunset, we strolled
from the Crescent set high above the town
to the bridge of honeyed stone, the river —
its slate silk now a mirror of paradise.
Later, the full moon climbing her window…
But my embrace could only comfort:

notes on
Elinor

we were lovers locked inside a cliché —
the pure secrecy of our bond a constant
aphrodisiac, while her husband's desire
to kill her slid an adamantine wall
between us — so hurt and enraged was she.
Then long months of it: my journeys to Bath —
there, our circling each other — her mind
still trapped in the labyrinth of his mind...
Until the turning point: her plan — involving
a train, a police detective, a novel.
I watched as Elinor became Rosa;
and Rosa, Elinor. What could I do?
There was no stopping either of them.

8
Why am I on this train? To guard her against
seizures — as her devoted physician.
To be the reverse of murderer: the antidote
to her husband. And to await the moment
when the husk falls away, the lovers cleave
for the first time, in a silent, sealed room —
like this one. It's two o'clock. Her sea-green eyes
are open, her lips trace a slow smile as,
with constrained grace, I bend to kiss her hand.

ELINOR PIERCE

Love story

We've stayed apart in this small space, as agreed.
You are here to support me in this quest
for justice (spliced, I confess, with revenge);
to keep me alive, should my breathing falter.
So why, now that everything has turned to
danger, do I find myself answering
your deepest gaze with mine, offering you
my warmth and hope, my long-withheld ardour?
At last, one way or another, he is gone...
I undo garments, lift them like outworn selves
up over my hair which I unpin.
My body unmoulds to its own shape; I stand
and cup your face; your hands rest on mine.
You listen to my even, assured breath,
remembering, in this stillness, the waiting,
the impossibility. Together
we fall through sun-speared aquamarine.
On the seabed, lying bathed in drowned light,
      we are the shell's dual clasp;
      we are the pearl dreaming itself.

FLORENCE ELLESMERE

Love p. to Mario

Why am I thinking of him tonight?
I lost him long ago — the illusionist
and master of escape, Mario Scampare.
When, that mist-veiled autumn day — the year
was 1883 — he left to perform
his most daring feat in the palace dungeons
of King Ludovico of Bravuria,
I felt he would triumph — but not return.
So it proved. Yet never did he forsake me.
What though my mind's eye saw him manacled, in a
locked cage, on some far island?
Night after night his spirit was near,
fortifying me as I withstood
the insults of Lord Eustace Wartington
with undimmed eyes then walked ramrod-straight
towards the footlights — the broken pearl necklace
in my hands, a shattered life...
                              Years vanished.
I no longer craved Mario's return
but carried his image at my centre —
an aspiring figure pressed always against
the limits of self; my muse; my absent lover.
With his unseen companionship, and the bright
words and wings of Dolores, shall I uncode —
at fleeting moments — the starlit globe of the future?

ERNEST WATTS *Baffled*

Two hours till dawn. My moment of truth draws near.
On this lonely night-watch, no headway with
the present case, yet I'm starting to fit
the pieces together — to understand
how I became who, and what, I am…
There had to be a reason — so I thought,
when a young man — why my life was as it was:
a pot of stone soup on an unlit stove.
But never could I find it. All questions
led to culs-de-sac; all explanations
proved chimerical; each clue I pursued
left me stranded in a fog-bound wasteland.
Thus my fascination with unsolved crimes,
sealed mysteries, began — as I tracked
the secret of my own life at a remove.
Why, I asked my twenty-year-old self,
had I not known a moment's peace or grace?
Why, when I spoke my truest thoughts,
did my tongue feel like sodden cardboard?
And why oh why hadn't I dared ever
to fall in love? Was the germ of the malaise
in the way my mother watched me — watched
my eyes, my hands: always, as though it were
her life's work. A watched pot never boils.
The heart-shaped stone grows colder… Years on,

my youth a grey memory, I apprised
my mother's secret — and thereby, part of mine.
My last image of her, dying, was of
drained lips, all-seeing eyes. *Rest in peace...*
My fingers drew down papery eyelids,
like holland blinds over windows still
glinting with twilight. *May you rest in peace —*
I certainly can't.
                    Months later,
sorting through her effects, I found no clue.
Then, at the back of a creaky drawer,
an old key gave itself into my hand.
Still more days of search till I beheld,
eye to eye, the lock it belonged to:
on a door, hidden by purple drapes,
behind her monumental four-post bed.
I entered a room filled with objects
laid out upon altars of crimson plush —
each one precious, all of them stolen:
a glittering catalogue of desire.
Audaciously, a raven watched from a shelf
of pearl necklaces — a presiding spirit,
its eyes ambiguously bright and dull,
as hers had been. The room posed the question:
Would I, too, become a thief? Was this
why her gaze had probed me with its double
message of fear, of hope? Would I, too,

brilliantly subvert appearances:
the god Hermes quicksilvering these
stubby fingers, making my soulful eyes
sharp with appetite for unearned gain?
And would *my* golden shame be hidden
in a veiled room of utterly useless
small wonders locked in sunless splendour?
We had lived, my mother Merle and I,
in a neatly decaying house, on funds
left by my father. She spoke of him once only,
her eyes glazed but tearless, explaining
he had died in a boating accident —
her voice almost inaudible, so that
I, a timid eight-year-old, wondered
if she had said, 'a batting accident'.
Or was it, in fact, a biting accident?
Maybe even, a baiting accident?
(I conjured a man in cricket-whites
mooring a tall yacht then leaping on shore
to curb a rabid dog; nearby, a trap
with iron jaws…) Her whispered tale became,
faute de mieux, my one rite of passage
into life's slippery miracle.
To compensate for my uncertainty,
I grew like a tree with branches too straight
ever to dip and sway with the wind.
Finally — aged thirty, key in hand —

Ernest's resolve

I gazed through a silver oval at
my forlorn *gravitas*, and vowed to be
interesting, or die. I walked with a limp,
topiaried my hair into odd shapes,
invented quirks and tics, wore screamingly
loud check scarves and measle-spotted bow-ties.
Forswearing my life as a clerk I worked
as a stable hand, a night watchman,
then as a dogsbody at a circus
where, for one glorious night, the clown's
apprentice stepped into the clown's long shoes.
My face became a custard pie! I fell
over and over myself! I was happy!
My taste for limelight whetted, I served as
a prompter at the Adelphi Theatre,
learning by heart an adaptation of
Conan Doyle's *A Scandal in Bohemia*.
As I sat concealed, mouthing Sherlock's
steely words, I felt myself enter
his mind and begin to see the world through
Holmes-coloured spectacles. So it was
I discovered my true vocation —
by a strange curve of logic ending up
as a Detective in Scotland Yard's
Criminal Investigation Department.
Thus my unbending rigour found
its place, while I had learned to flow with life…

*his true
vocation*

One problem remained. Because I was,
in my person, so unusual now
I needed to become usual again —
or seem to — which I did with a vengeance:
embracing the colour brown at all times;
a fly on the wall which leaves no fly spots.
My work prospered — till the present crisis.
On this fateful journey, I find myself —
an expert at solving mysteries —
lost in a labyrinth I helped create.
For who, exactly, is the victim here?
(I suspected, at first, it might be me…)
Once the victim is known, I can find
the murderer. But at this moment
clouds of confusion beset me.
Should I apply cold logic, as would
Sherlock Holmes, mesmerised by pipe-smoke?
No! I will wade on through this treacle
of doubt, despair and disappointed love…
Somewhere inside my mind there's a gold key
to a room of secrets, revelations.
If I become as the keen-eyed jackdaw
I shall see it — that key of light trembling,
soon to fall from the damson heart of a rose.

CLAIRE WESTWOOD

Gwendolyn, my doll, clings to me.
I want the sky with its hundreds of stars
to be wrapped around this sleeping train
like a soft blue blanket, a twinkling cocoon.
We are travelling so fast I can't be still
but inside myself, I am waiting...
For sweet, bright days, and nights full of stories —
firelight dancing in Gwen's eyes as she listens.

My mother rests, pretending to sleep,
her golden hair spread out on the pillow.
I'll watch till her eyes open... But no —
she's deep asleep, her breathing slow and calm,
the blanket curved like a dolphin's back.

I dreamt of a small boat with sky-blue sail
rocking and sliding over foam-toothed waves,
heading who knows where.
                              Sky-blue sail...
who knows where?
                    How peaceful her face looks.
Is she dreaming?
                    Ticketty clack, tyclack.
The train is swaying, going faster, faster.
The wind whispers its secrets into my ear.

RIVER OF LIFE, RIVER OF DEATH

'River of Life, River of Death'

by Rosa Morland

It was New Year's Eve. Keeping her lone vigil, Laura sat by the fire. Above its rippling veil of flames she saw the nightmare image that had begun to haunt her: of a woman, herself, running down a dark road towards high iron gates that opened to admit her then clanged shut, locking her in.

To Laura, it seemed a vision of her future. In three days she must move with Bess and Sam, her small children, to Selby. She would work in the flour-mill while Maria, her married sister, looked after the children. The struggle to provide for them through her work as a cottage weaver had failed. Even with the vegetables she grew, the fish she took from the river, they could not survive here.

At midnight she went to stand by the window, looking down at the river Ouse then at the full moon, its creamy silver smudged with grey. She could barely see, must half-imagine, the long sweep of hills sloping into the dales, now great wells of shadow. High on her right, the railway bridge stretched out, joining the hillside less than two hundred yards away from her cottage.

River, bridge, sky... An absolute silence.

Suddenly, tearing that silence apart, the late express train to Scotland possessed the bridge, the night, puffing out a long plume of steam then quickly vanishing. Usually, Laura heard it only in her sleep. Now, in less than a minute, the scene was restored to her intact. She breathed calmly, drawing its peace into the depths of her being.

Yet something had changed. Laura was aware of a clot of darkness on one of the iron rafters above the centre of the bridge — a human figure! Slowly he climbed down to the rail tracks then, limping and stopping often to clutch his left shoulder, made his way towards the nearer end — the one on her side of the river.

When he was almost there, a clumsy step caused him to stumble and fall through a break in the railing, plummeting past the web of struts beneath the bridge, to the river. He disappeared through its turbulent black surface.

Without hesitation Laura put on her cloak and ran down the stone steps set into the hillside; turning left, she made for the long rope tethered beside the water's edge. If he surfaced again, if the river was not too fast, if he were not too far out... there was just a chance.

Seconds later she caught a glimpse of a white face surrounded by wild black hair: the man was borne along by the flood, his right arm clamped on a piece of driftwood. The other arm, seemingly lifeless, was unable to help him strike out for the river's edge.

Laura turned with desperate haste to uncoil the rope, grasp it in readiness. She waved her arms, yelled out 'Here! Over Here!' again and again. He let go of the driftwood and began to swim sidestroke towards the shore. Now he was approaching the stretch of water by which she stood. Her foot wedged against a rock, she called at the top of her voice and threw the line. He reached out, missed the rope, floundered, caught it. His powerful body writhed, twisting him inside the end of the rope; she began to pull with all her might.

As he drew near, gasping, it was as if Laura could see deeper and deeper into his eyes — till she saw the eyes of the man she had once saved from the river at this very place. He had become her husband. It was he who had driven the stake into the riverbank and tied the rope to it, commemorating his rescue. But in the end it had not saved him: the river had claimed his drunken, raging body one moonless night — delivering her from what it had, bitter years ago, yielded up to her.

But now, still, every moment counted, every ounce of her strength was needed to help this unknown man. He was almost there! Next thing, Laura felt him grasp her outstretched hand then wrench her into the dark water while, with his right arm coiled in the rope, he searched for a foothold to the shore.

Down she sped towards the treacherous bend in the river — there was no chance of saving herself if she went much further. Feeling its dead weight, Laura undid her cloak, let it go. With her remaining strength she swam towards the great willow tree sloping out from the river's edge, knowing there was a raised stretch of riverbed near its roots. Fish-shapes of water swirled around her, hemming her in. Her feet touched bottom.

Once clear of the river, Laura looked back along the shore. He was not there. Then she saw him still floundering, a few yards from the bank. Would the mercurial current help or hinder him?

Suddenly her gaze was distracted by a dark shape borne along swiftly and silently — a tree trunk arrowing downstream. As it passed under the bridge, a reef of cloud briefly covered the moon which then shone again on the river, silvering its blackness.

The tree trunk seemed headed for the struggling man, but the current pulled it away. However, a sudden turn towards the bridge had meant he saw it looming without knowing what it was. He screamed, his mouth filling with water, panic causing him to lose his grip on the rope. Swept out to the middle of the river, he was carried ineluctably by the vast, whispering onrush towards the skein of currents at the river bend.

Laura's eyes followed the struggling figure till they saw only blank darkness. Nothing could be done now. She turned resolutely away, thinking only of her children, dismissing all thoughts of his fate. Laura would always remember that hand taking possession of hers and pulling — wilfully, she had no doubt — until she slipped: exchanging his danger for her already diminished safety.

Her feet were taking her back along the riverbank; her chilled, dripping form climbed the steps to the cottage. She saw, with renewed gratitude, the heavy wreath of brier-roses arched over its door. The moon shone with stark intensity over the whole scene. It seemed to her now like a great luminous peach — dented and bruised, as if hard, determined fingers had pressed deep into its flesh.

Back inside her home, Laura hurriedly took off her clothes, dried herself, put on her nightdress and dressing-gown. She rekindled the almost dead fire. Entering their bedroom, she gazed through the dimness at Bess and Sam, nested beneath their counterpane. When the fire was strong again, she moved her chair nearer the hearth and rested, saying prayers of thanks, prayers of hope. Until dawn came Laura sat by the fire, watching images from the past dance and die in the flames, and new images of the future press into life above a wavering blue film of heat.

The Mystery of Rosa Morland

AT WAVERLEY STATION

SEAMUS L'ESTRANGE

1
We waited to meet him, as agreed.
I looked at light sculpting the chrome teapot
on the table between Elinor and me
then at her face, open yet wary.
Small wraiths curled and twisted above our cups...
Watts, we could see, was still detained by
the incident outside our carriage.
A bearish man in lordly attire had grabbed
a woman with veiled face as she stepped from the train:
he roared, pushed her away, turned to glimpse
the second veiled woman, in similar
exquisite clothes, weaving towards them.
Once in clear view of the scene, she stopped — too late!
His hand was on her arm. A third woman,
in midnight blue, sought to intervene
and was struck across the mouth for her pains.
Still more flour in the plot's gravy when
a red-haired man leapt from the train to defend
the women — savage blows were exchanged...
Watts, en route to meet us, had doubled back
to quell the fracas. Now he was questioning
all those involved, writing notes in his book.
We remained calm, Elinor and I,
thankful to be away from such turmoil

as we sat — precariously poised between
a shadowed past, an unwritten future.
A last glance back at our carriage showed
one blind raised on darkness, a young girl's face,
moon-pale, with shining eyes... Travellers ran,
doors slammed: the train about to head west.
Cloaked in royal blue, a woman went by
bearing a cage caped with the same velvet:
a gap hinted at jewel-bright plumage.
She stopped, set down the cage, massaged her hands.
A man clutching a satchel to his breast
doffed his hat in greeting and offered help:
lithe fingers gripped the cage's gold ring.
Together they walked towards the cabs.
Elinor sat as if in dream, her silence
a transparent veil...
              The train creaked, rolled past.
My finger was hooked in the handle of a cup,
holding me to earth as my eye followed
waftings of steam and smoke above the lamps.
Finally, Watts joined us — his face sombre,
eyes wearily alert. He put his notebook
on the stained table, drank some tea
then slowly raised his brown gaze to us.

2

As Watts summed up the facts, the fatal compartment took shape in the air between us:

A loud noise coming from it had alerted the passenger next door — who knocked, received no reply, went to ask the attendant to check on the occupant. The door was found to be unlocked, and the compartment empty; then he, Watts, was called.

There was an open suitcase on the seat, near the window. Some of its contents — mainly the shirts and undergarments — were in a chaotic heap; the topmost ones were blood-stained and, because the window was open, wet. Parts of the carpet and seat were also wet from the rain blowing in.

On the floor, the empty liquor bottle; its neck had been broken off, but was nowhere in the room.

There were five cigar butts in the ashtray.

A search behind the seating yielded only an old postage stamp — foreign, showing a red castle with turrets piercing a cloud. But it could have been there for a long time.

And there were two novels: the first lay closed on the seat; the other — by Rosa Morland — in a very damaged state, lay in a corner.

As far as he could judge, nothing of value was obviously missing from Maldonbury's effects.

3

'So... was it murder, made to look like suicide?' Watts asked, a dour glint in his eye.

'Or suicide, made to look like murder?' countered Elinor.

'If murder,' said Watts, 'only one person could have devised it, as I read the situation. Help would have been needed to carry it through, of course.'

He looked directly at me. There was a difficult silence.

Elinor said: 'With the door unlocked, it could be either.' She toyed with her cup. 'What was in his luggage?'

Watts consulted his notebook. 'Along with the shirts and undergarments, there were pyjamas; stockings and two pairs of shoes; and, on the bottom of the case, formal evening attire. Also: a hairbrush, a clothes-brush and a manicure set — the scissors were in place, no trace of blood on them.'

'Razor and shaving-brush?'

'Yes. The razor was also clean. But he could have been cut, or cut himself, with the missing piece of glass.'

'What about his dressing-gown?'

'Not there.'

'Jerseys?'

'None.'

'Gloves?'

'His coat and hat were on the rack — no gloves were with them; nor a scarf.' Watts paused then added, 'When I rearranged the contents of the case after noting all items, it was half-full. He seems to have been travelling — relatively speaking — light.'

'That's something he never did. Eustace was — or is — a fop, a most fastidious man. And he'd never travel without his dressing-gown.'

4

'So, it could have been an escape — made to look like murder,' suggested Elinor. 'The dressing-gown — perhaps stuffed with jerseys as extra padding — to help cushion the fall and prevent freezing later on; the gloves to protect his hands. The scarf to help bind a vest around his self-inflicted wound.'

'Such a lot of blood!' replied Watts. 'And such a long way to jump — from such a very fast train... I'd see any attempt at escape as suicidal, whether he survived it or not. Long odds for a seasoned gambler?'

'Those were the odds Eustace always favoured. Besides which, he's a man of almost supernatural obduracy. I believe he'd stop at nothing to avoid being brought to account — legally, or even morally — for his attempt to end my life. (An attempt which, don't forget, almost succeeded!) Turning the tables, casting me in the murderer's role, would have seemed an ingenious way out. Also, it would be an act of revenge on me for evading the fate he so meticulously planned! You see, our marriage was, from the first, an unspoken battle...'

'I wonder who will win?' Watts interposed.

'Eustace always needed to win, could never bear not to — and it's brought him nothing but ruin. His massive gambling debts would have been a further reason for wanting to disappear. And on top of everything else, there have been damaging personal scandals.'

'So one might suppose from items in the newspapers. But the fact remains that what happened could now equally be — if your comments on the evidence of his clothes are truthful — an escape designed to look like murder, or a murder designed to look like an escape.'

'Maldonbury had many enemies.'

'Yes. My suspect would be a person who hated him, knew his habits intimately, and had at their disposition both brains and brawn...'

He glanced at me again. There was a tight silence. Then, with aplomb, Elinor poured more hot water into the pot.

'Some more tea?' she said, smiling.

5

Watts drank another cup of tea then stared at the galaxy of leaves inside his cup.

His report would suggest a suicide attempt, influenced by alcohol. Appearances, he said, tilting the thick white cup, *pointed that way to him. The tracks would be searched from Doncaster to Batley.*

'Then we'll see what we see…'

There was a long pause, after which he addressed Elinor.

'If Maldonbury is found alive, will you pursue your complaint against him?'

She lifted the pot, poured the dregs into her cup.

'No. It's finished now.'

6

As Watts hesitated, Elinor spoke again.

'And what of our midnight meeting with Maldonbury?'

The detective's hands lay flat as cards on the table; his gaze held hers for a long minute.

'I've come to the conclusion that, while it would serve truth to set down every fact, it would not serve life. During the small hours, I believed the net of investigation must be cast as widely as possible. Whatever the consequences. But now it seems most likely that, in the end, I might catch only a single rogue barracuda.'

'That could still bite holes in the net and escape?'

'Maybe. My work is not yet finished.'

'Or try to drown those holding the net? If he's found alive, he'll tell of our meeting. It would look like a conspiracy. And if we were seen and heard...'

'We were.'

'And you'll take that chance? Apart from anything else, you'd be professionally ruined.'

'Yes, I've chosen. The story now has an almost pleasing symmetry. Or do I mean, asymmetry?'

Watts turned to me.

'We are never cured of life's risk — as you, more than any of us, know.'

I stood to shake his hand after he rose to go.

He looked at Elinor simply, then bowed.

Though he paused in the great doorway, he did not look back.

I would like to have taken a photograph of him in that moment of loss, or second thoughts mastered, among the throng of travellers and porters and flower sellers, mist meeting the dawn light, and the wet road beyond.

BIOGRAPHIES

Jasper Abbott

Born in 1845, Jasper grew up in a house on Crooms Hill, Greenwich, within view of the Royal Observatory. As a boy he was fascinated by the night sky and studied the planets and stars. Later, he developed an obsession with time and, at the age of sixteen, was apprenticed to the firm of Taylor and Wolsey, Clockmakers. In due course, he became a member of the Worshipful Company of Clockmakers. Bringing a high level of artistry to his work, he was known for the delicacy of his metal embellishments and his frequent use of sun, moon and star motifs.

A deeply introverted man, Jasper thought of himself as too unsociable ever to marry. For much of his adult life, he lived at home with his mother, Muriel, whom he cared for in her old age. (His father, Cedric, had died when he was eleven.) A year after Muriel died (in December, 1899), Jasper travelled to Edinburgh to make a fresh start. In this phase of his life he found great pleasure in returning to his passion for astronomy, observing the drama of the heavens with a powerful telescope he had designed and constructed himself.

At this time Jasper also tasted the more convivial joys of life, joining the circle of spiritualists and theatre people who had gathered around the psychic, Florence Ellesmere. He often sipped tea in a corner of her leafy parlour on Saturday afternoons when she held a salon, staying on for a quiet chat when the other, dazzlingly flamboyant or bafflingly secretive guests had departed.

After Florence's early death in 1907, Jasper withdrew for a time from the social circle that had surrounded her, then once more visited the theatres of Edinburgh to see plays acted, written or directed by his friends, and went for Sunday outings in the Esk valley with acquaintances from the spiritualist world who, seemingly against type, loved a picnic.

On the latter occasions he brought along Dolores, the macaw bequeathed to him by Florence. Sometimes her voice — abrasive or lyrical, depending on her mood — issued from a cluster of oak leaves, or descended from her bright form overhead: a colourful counterpoint to the ethereal conversations below, wafting over heather, meadow and stream.

Jasper Abbott is remembered for the many fine clocks he fashioned during his professional life. One of his mystery clocks may be seen in the Clock Museum in Vienna; and several of his skeleton clocks, as well as a silver clock in the shape of a rose, are in the Museum of the Worshipful Company of Clockmakers, Guildhall, London. He is also remembered for a modification to a telescope design that was patented in 1903, and for a flower-clock in the Royal Botanic Garden in Edinburgh, created in 1908 to honour the memory of Florence Ellesmere.

Aurora Adenay

The third daughter of Sir Crispian and Lady Freda Adenay of Hawling Manor, Surrey. At the age of eighteen she enjoyed a dazzling London season, after which she rather mischievously married the bulbous and beetroot-coloured Lord Lambert McRossiter — a patently absurd choice, though his membership of the Peerage meant that the marriage received her parents' enthusiastic blessing.

Aurora settled into a life of labyrinthine social and sexual intrigue, indulging in racy gossip, and frequently acting in such a way as to be an object of it. Her affairs were as flagrant as her husband's complexion, yet her accomplished air of innocence kept all retribution in abeyance.

In the year of 1901, however, she fled to Venice after her husband assaulted her on Waverley Station, Edinburgh, following the unravelling of one of her more ambitious intrigues. Thus she had the triumph of extracting a magnificent settlement from McRossiter, while relishing her exit from British upper class society, whose possibilities for amusement she felt she had exhausted.

Aurora settled permanently in Venice, where she enjoyed the glamour of being viewed as exotic and the prestige endowed by rumours that she had been a famous courtesan in London (who favoured the powerful Duke of Warrickfield, or Sir Henry Radcliffe, Chairman of the Bank of England — or was it the Prime Minister himself?). Wherever these rumours came from — yet other rumours claimed they issued from her very self — she remained incandescently aloof, despite being much sought after by ageing, eminent men.

She had a great love of opera and frequented *La Fenice* theatre, sitting always in the same prominent, subtly lit box, alone. However, the tide of fascination began to ebb when it was discovered, as late as 1909, that she was driven by a compulsion to seek lovers who were the counterparts of characters in the famous operas she so ardently viewed.

All very well in the case of the Count Almavivas and Dukes of Mantua of this world, but it was understood she was particularly attracted by the more humbly-origined, more youthful and muscular characters. This quest involved a certain amount of travel, and there had been, for instance, two discreet trips to Seville and its vicinity. And she was no stranger to the Latin Quarter of Paris. Amorous pages, quick-witted barbers, starving poets and painters... love was truly the great leveller for Aurora, Lady McRossiter.

Over the years the god Eros was to reward her tireless and somewhat original efforts on his behalf by casting a veil of agelessness about her. The soft light and watery reflections of Venice were a compassionate accompaniment to her journey into the later phases of life when she was attended by the gigolo, and the faithful retainer in youthful guise.

Aurora remained a valued curiosity in Venice. She was, to members of the higher echelons of Venetian society, both different from them, and the same. They knew her, yet… they didn't know her. The situation was, in a word, satisfying all round. What more fitting fate could she have asked for?

Dolores

Dolores, a scarlet macaw, began life in a rainforest near Florencia, Columbia, in 1885. At the age of one she was netted by a bird-catcher and travelled to England on board *The Winged Adventurer*. Her extreme youth made her particularly susceptible to acquiring a second language, and she instinctively reproduced many nautical phrases in the course of her journey, at first with a sense of play and novelty, later with a dawning understanding of their meaning.

After *The Winged Adventurer* docked at Bristol, Dolores was sold to an innkeeper, Stanley Paxton. Thus she became the resident wit and scourge at *The Lobster Pot*, embracing a whole new patois with gusto. However, as her knowledge of the import of her words grew, Dolores began to suffer from bouts of brooding silence.

When Stanley put out feelers in the hope of acquiring another, more reliably vocal parrot, he soon found himself in possession of Jack, a scarlet macaw from Bolivia. He planned to keep Dolores along with Jack, as he was fond of her and took a sympathetic attitude to her swings between eloquence and muteness. Perhaps the two macaws would provide companionship for each other?

The edgily cryptic conversations between them that he sometimes overheard, suggested to the optimistic Stanley a mutual desire for further rapport. He wondered if there might, in due course, be a third — then maybe a fourth, a fifth — macaw? So, before lights out each night, he made ready the conditions for the courtship and union of Dolores and Jack by leaving their cage doors open in the now empty and soundless inn.

Weeks passed. Stanley took the presence of occasional feathers scattered on the bar counter as evidence that his hopes had some foundation. However, creeping down one night to get some Madeira to assuage sleeplessness, Stanley heard words, then encountered a scene, which decisively put an end to his dreams. One of his macaws would have to go.

The tough, salty-tongued Jack was clearly more suited to the life of an inn by the docks. A few days later, Dolores took the fancy of a raffish-looking individual just off a ship from Spain, who presented himself as the Earl of Hurtleforth. Stanley had misgivings about the man because of his drooping left eyelid and strange smell, but upon being told Dolores would be given to his daughter, Annabella, sold her to him.

At Falconspur, Dolores was indeed the pet of Annabella, a most impudent child, and from the moment of meeting her began to plan an escape. After weeks of misery, she used the occasion of being sought by Grimalkin, the estate's overfed but insatiable cat, to burst from her cage — first terrifying Grimalkin with an unholy squawk — then fly through the open French windows. Dolores circled over the spacious grounds before exploring further afield. Eventually she caught sight of a great elm between a cottage and reed-fringed brook, and touched down on one of its branches.

If this was not paradise as she had once known it, nevertheless the setting pleased her, and her spirit revived. After resting, Dolores tasted the joy of flying for its own wondrous sake, ascending and swooping with elegance and verve. The rhythmic flow of her wings was, as always, subtly and agreeably audible to her. Openness, space, freedom of movement... and the consolations of direct, though admittedly weak, sunlight. This happiness would last for seven days.

A voluminous woman dressed in foxglove purple was alighting from a carriage outside the cottage. She stood at its green door for a moment then — rather than deploying the doorknocker — screamed. The occupant, a pale man with sad dark eyes who was now well-known to Dolores, opened the door and the woman disappeared inside.

Ah, curiosity! — and those fateful moments when we risk what we most love to satisfy it... Dolores soon found herself on the lowest branch of a lime tree close to an open window; from there she stepped onto the window sill. The woman's back was turned to her as she gabbled of dark doings in the village, hated neighbours, and then, with triumph, the acquisition of a room of oriental knick-knacks collected by the recently deceased Lord Soddington.

In the large mirror over the mantelpiece, Mrs Gladys Flintlock saw herself, her brother Kingsley Steele — the never-forgotten because never-remembered author of the poetry volume, *Night Thoughts from an Autumn Garden* — and Dolores. Still speaking, she rose and walked to the other window of the sitting room, seemingly intent on re-arranging the curtains. Then — as if out of nowhere! — there was a swift, sweeping movement as Gladys, having surreptitiously picked up

Kingsley's butterfly net, pounced on Dolores whose wildly flapping wings resisted the enclosing mesh in vain. An old trauma re-enacted; history repeating itself...

So began Dolores' incarceration among the knick-knacks of Lord Soddington and countless other collectors of odd-shaped nothingness in *The Trinket Box*, Mrs Flintlock's shop in the main street of Whernleigh, and in her crowded parlour. Ear-trumpets blocked by fluff, sneezed-upon snuff boxes, chipped ivory fans, porcelain dancers reaching out with half an arm or raising a footless leg: these were her stock in trade and had progressively colonised each dust-matted nook and corner of her house. Unnervingly, a hundred clocks struck at erratic intervals throughout the day and night, answering or upstaging or repudiating each other, the loftier ones attempting Socratic dialogues with silence.

In the parlour, a macaw identical to Jack was perched perpetually on a pot plant stand, a brown maidenhair fern set as if in mockery beside him. At night, if and when the hearth yielded more fire than smoke, those glazed eyes opened to depths of memory. Nearby, a fan-shaped display of peacock feathers rose from a sepulchral marble vase.

In *The Trinket Box*, as morning light struck the tall glass case in which finches, larks, owls, ravens and eagles perched on grey sticks, Dolores saw reflections of her own eyes superimposed on their vanquished, lacklustre eyes. In the face of such erasure, escape was imperative! But patience, cunning and resourcefulness would be needed...

On the small stone bridge leading out of Whernleigh, Dolores rested. Only ten minutes ago, she had stretched her aching wings into flight, sweeping over the village as its denizens sat in the church of St Barnabas the Younger. It was Sunday morning, the bells had rung, and as usual, Mrs Gladys Flintlock occupied most of her designated pew, with her antiquarian page-marker snug inside an exceedingly rare edition of the Bible, its leather cover scuffed and key-holed by time. In the back row sat Bart Preston, the chimney-sweep recently employed by Mrs Flintlock — a small-boned youth who also helped out with thatching repairs around the district.

Dolores hoped she had flown all the soot out of her feathers by now... That long black tunnel — such a difficult birth! Her exit from her cage had been even more tricky, but with the help of a brass paper-knife — drawn by her beak through the bars then clamped under her left wing until it could be deployed — she had battled through the night with the malevolent clasp of her cage, and won. Now, a new cycle was about to begin...

It was on Whernleigh bridge that a contractor with a load of lime pellets and sawdust bound for London's theatres and music-halls, saw Dolores and, acting on a whim, placed her without coercion on the seat of his cart. His name was Rory Grimsby. Dolores relished the journey with its shimmering visions of towns and countryside, workers in the fields and ambling villagers — not to mention a fascinating range of bird life. Within three hours she was outside the Adelphi Theatre, waddling up and down the cart-horse's back and flexing her wings while a delivery was being made.

At that point, a young actress, Sylvia Court, noticed Dolores. Costumed as a servant girl for a dress rehearsal, she impulsively stole her and hid her in a storeroom. Thus it was that Dolores became the mascot of The Travelling Players, and would frequent London's West End and tour Britain, visiting its finest theatres, for many years.

Despite her affection for Sylvia, Dolores became particularly attached to Florence Ellesmere, the company's leading actress, and went with her to Edinburgh at the beginning of 1901. There, Dolores proved an excellent helpmeet to Florence in her new vocation as a psychic, sometimes providing a word that was eluding her, or inventing a useful distraction when Florence needed time to think. She lived in a relatively leafy environment, as many luxuriant plants flourished along the walls and on shelves throughout Florence's warm house. Frequent jaunts into the countryside permitted of those experiences of free flight that had been painfully rare in Dolores' life.

After the untimely death of Florence in 1907, Dolores lived with Jasper Abbott — uneasily at first, but increasingly enjoying her role as the companion of his hours spent gazing at the night sky, and learning by degrees to tolerate the rest. When Jasper's time came to join the stars, she disappeared. Her further adventures are beyond the scope of this present summary of her history.

Florence Ellesmere

Born into a theatrical family in 1862, (at *The Rovers' Inn*, near Cheadle in Cheshire), Florence trod the boards from the age of three. While her father, Jeremy, was a renowned actor-manager, her mother, Isabella, was a singer of vivacious temperament, her style particularly suited to the music-hall — she was a darling of the patrons at the Victoria Palace for several decades.

After reaching adulthood, Florence toured as principle actress in her father's company around Britain, when not starring in plays in the West End. Her most acclaimed roles were as Lady Christabel Wartington in

The Pearl Necklace, and as Irene Adler in an adaptation of Sir Arthur Conan Doyle's 'A Scandal in Bohemia'.

She retired from the stage in 1900, and thereafter established herself in Edinburgh as a psychic, offering readings of the crystal ball and Tarot cards. Florence flourished in this role for some years, without any of the negative notoriety she had feared, and able to rest from the intense public gaze suffered in her life as an actress. However, she did not embrace isolation and had a wide circle of friends for whom she held a salon each Saturday afternoon.

While making only modest claims for her gifts as a psychic, and stressing the importance of plain speaking and an earthy realism in her work, Florence became increasingly subject to tranced states, which often persisted for long periods. She had been in one of these for six days before she died of unknown causes in 1907.

Her passing was mourned by her many intimates and her devoted friend, Jasper Abbott, who took her parrot, Dolores, to live with him — in accordance with instructions in Florence's will. At this time, Dolores herself entered a tranced state which lasted for many days. However, a domestic accident in which Jasper burned himself while pouring tea, caused a shriek of profane hilarity to issue forth from her beak, after which her sometimes barbed, but oddly illuminating, comments were again frequently to be heard. The pair reached an understanding, bonded by their love for Florence.

Seamus L'Estrange

Seamus was born in Italy in 1861. His Irish mother, Maud McGonagle, had been a dancer before her marriage. His father, Victor, served in the French diplomatic service in Turin, the first capital of the newly proclaimed Italy, and later in Rome.

As a young man he studied medicine in Paris, then crossed the English Channel to settle in the small coastal village of Tredding Cress, five miles from Worthing, so as to avoid the pressures of cosmopolitan life and pursue his interest in nature and photography. While remaining a somewhat unreadable figure in the eyes of the local community, he was accepted and respected for his work as a doctor.

At the end of 1900 he left Tredding Cress and, after marrying Elinor Pierce in Edinburgh, began a new life with her in the town of Dunkeld in Perthshire, again practising as a doctor and indulging his passion for photography in his spare hours. The latter diminished, however, as he became in time the father of Elizabeth and Samuel, to whom he was devoted. He died under an oak tree in the middle of a lightning storm, in 1942.

A folio of his distinctive and, in some cases, disquieting photographs can be found in the archives of Innerpeffray Library. In particular, his studies of Birnam Wood, often taken at dawn or dusk, are valued for both their poetic power and documentary precision.

Alasdair Lockhart

Born in 1872, Alasdair grew up in Edinburgh, the youngest in a family of five sons. As all of his brothers — Angus, Malcolm, Guy and Everard — and his father, Herbert, graced the legal profession, often as a boy he heard conversations conducted in Latin in his home. This was to prove helpful to him in later life when he pursued the study of natural history — after having decided to spend his life contemplating the laws of nature rather than those laid down by human society.

In this the influence of his mother, Serena, had its part to play. When not attending to the welfare of her family, she spent her time in a large, high-domed observatory full of ferns, orchids and birds. There she passed her days painting, reading novels, and conversing with her many canaries, doves and parrots.

Alasdair was to choose bird life as the special focus of his work as a naturalist, with journeys to countries such as Finland, Argentina and Tibet, during which many varieties of birds were recorded by him in written and pictorial form. In particular, his documentation of the rare owl parrot, the kakapo, native to New Zealand's South Island, was highly valued in the light of its near-extinction. This parrot has survived, if slenderly, to the present day, when careful hopes are held for its survival.

In 1901, Alasdair married Charlotte Winter. They lived in a cottage by a stream outside Grangemouth, northwest of Edinburgh, when not abroad on one of their many journeys in pursuit of rare species of birds.

Lambert McRossiter

The only son of Lord Oswald and Lady Caroline McRossiter, of Rumbervie Castle in Rossvale, Midlothian, and Turrets in Kensington, London. Along with his father's title of Viscount, Lambert inherited these properties at the age of thirty, and proceeded to run them down over the next forty years. His addiction to extravagant living was the main cause of the near-extinction of his fortune, along with a large settlement paid under duress to his wife, Aurora, after they separated permanently in 1901. Soon after that event, he resolved never to remarry, but rather to make other arrangements, as indeed he always had.

Famous for his riding skills in his youth, Lambert became, by virtue of his enormous appetite for victuals, so huge in bulk that, by the age of thirty-five, mounting a horse proved impossible. After this he devoted himself exclusively to eating, drinking wine and spirits, and gaming.

Eustace Vivian Maldonbury

Baron Eustace Maldonbury was the second son of a family whose wealth was founded on the importation of sugar and coffee from the West Indies. His palatial home, Heathwick Hall, was near Worthing in West Sussex.

His only brother, Anthony, died on his twenty-first birthday, after opening a letter at his desk. Though the letter proffered congratulations, the sender's signature was indecipherable, covered as it was by a verdigris-like stain encrusted with the body of a crushed insect. It was assumed that an unusual death by poisoning had occurred, but whether it was accidental, or intentional on the part of Anthony, or persons unknown, remained unclear.

Educated at Eton and at King's College, Cambridge, Eustace's main interests were Classical Literature, and Philosophy — the cultivation of a rarified intelligence being of importance to him in upstaging more long-standing, or higher ranking, members of the aristocracy. Despite his membership of three London clubs, Lord Maldonbury was not a sociable man, his personal style in company tending to ennui and irritation. On his frequent trips to London he spent his time orchestrating and transacting liaisons with society women, and in the gaming-rooms of his clubs.

He was married three times, in each case to strong-minded women whom he desired to tame. His first wife, Alexandra, died in an accident involving the overturning of a carriage taking her from their home to the railway station. When his second wife, Hortense, died in a riding accident — the horse being so strangely excited afterwards that it had to be shot — Oscar Wilde was heard to declare at the Albermarle Club: 'To lose one wife in an accident might look like Providence; to lose two, suggests the possibility of earthly rather than divine intervention.'

Elinor, the Baron's third wife, disappeared on the last day of 1899, and was thought to have fallen off a cliff and drowned. During the following year, Lord Maldonbury was often heard to mention while at one or other of his clubs — with a kind of triumphal glee, as if delivering an unanswerable riposte to the now disgraced Wilde, (who would be dead by December) — that he had been 'in another country' at the time of his third wife's death, with 'a pristine, soon-to-be-conquered summit in his sights, and a limitless white kingdom beneath him'.

Lord Maldonbury jumped, fell or was pushed from a speeding train soon after midnight, on the first day of the twentieth century. While foul play was suspected, the facts established by a police inspector who happened to be on board the train were inconclusive. Though suicide was strongly considered a possible explanation by him, Maldonbury's body was never found. An investigative visit to an Edinburgh brothel, after the Baron's secret ownership of it came to light, produced no leads. Subsequent rumours of sightings on the Continent — at grand hotels, spas and casinos — had their day in the clubs and salons of London society, but no substantial evidence was ever produced as to his existence continuing after the time of his disappearance.

Anne Morgan

Anne Morgan was born on a farm outside Aberystwyth in 1878, the second of nine children. When she was fifteen, Anne went into service with the Pemberton family, of Dulwich, London, helping to look after their four children and doing household tasks. After five years, she moved to the Kensington residence of Lord McRossiter, where she was a personal maid to Lady McRossiter, while doubling as parlour-maid.

During a visit to her family at the beginning of 1901, Anne asked to stay at home to help with her younger siblings, as her mother's health was poor, and she herself did not wish to return to service. Later, Anne worked in the draper's shop in Aberystwyth where she became friends with John Davies, the proprietor's son. Married in 1906, they lived in a small house with a view of Cardigan Bay.

Rosa Morland

The prolific author, Rosa Morland, refused ever to allow any information regarding her self or her life to be conveyed to the reading public. Lacking any details themselves, except for a box number at Brighton Post Office and, after the turn of the century, one at the General Post Office in Perth, her publishers, Cavendish and Pallant, had no option but to respect her wishes. On her death, a letter to them cited several literary works for which *noms de plume* had been used. (The publishers were Quirk and Ransom.) These titles are accordingly appended to the following list of novels by Rosa Morland.

Chamber of Shadows, 1893; *The Man with Glass Fingers*, 1894; *The Double Life of Dora Lombard*, 1895; *Silhouette of a Murder*, 1896; *Last Train from Charlton*, 1897; *The Face in the Locket,* 1898; *The Secret of Bloodstone Castle,* 1900; *Laura Osmund: A Woman of the Dales,* 1902; *The Fawnfield Chronicles,* 1903; *The Notorious Mrs Merrivule,* 1905; *The Burlington Sapphires,* 1907; *Footprints in the Maze,* 1909; *The Ghost of La Fenice,* 1910; *Serena Lockhart Boards the Paris Express,* 1912; *Murder Out of Time,* 1914; *The Black Gardenia,* 1920; *Blood on the Croquet Lawn,* 1922; *The Glyndebourne Inheritance,* 1924; *The Case of the Poisoned Cameo,* 1926; *Death in a Brown Study,* 1928; *The Affair of the Tongue-Tied Parrot,* 1936; *Leonore Pryce Investigates,* 1938; *The Wind Shall Be My Winding Sheet,* 1941; *Bury Me in Amber,* 1943; *Once on a Starry Midnight,* 1945.

Works published under *noms de plume*:

As Aubrey L. Mander:
Lord Rutherton's Revenge, 1899; *The Vanishing of Raymond Bellamy,* 1901; *The Sleeping Car Murders,* 1904; *A Mirror Reversed,* 1906.

As Merlin A. Ross:
A Scandal in Bohemia, (an adaption for the stage of Sir Arthur Conan Doyle's story), 1893; *The Pearl Necklace,* (a play), 1896.

Elinor Pierce

Born in Worthing in 1870, Elinor was a twin whose identical sister, who would be called Jane, did not survive her birth.

A dreamy, solitary child, she loved walking by the sea in all weathers, and sitting by the fire in winter, reading. Elinor was educated at home by her mother, Kathleen, and her grandmother, Róis Ó Muratain, who had travelled to England from Ireland at the time of the Great Famine. Róis was known for her gifts as a storyteller, which she passed on to Elinor.

On reaching the age of sixteen, Elinor decided to become a school teacher and found employment at a school in Worthing. Over the next few years she devoted herself to her pupils, and followed her passion for country walking at the weekends.

It was while walking through some woods near Heathwick Hall, an estate some three miles from Worthing, that Elinor was one day set upon by a poacher. She was saved from serious harm by Baron Eustace Maldonbury, then returning from a hunting expedition. His solicitous charm made a strong impression on Elinor. Subsequent encounters, which she assumed to be accidental, led to a friendship. The couple's wedding took place six months after their first meeting. As Lord Maldonbury had already been married and widowed twice, Elinor became, at the age of twenty-two, the third Baroness Maldonbury.

But the marriage was an unhappy one, as it soon became evident that a shared love of books had been the only real bridge between the pair. Moreover, Elinor, who had never disguised her independence of mind, found her strong opinions increasingly antagonised her husband. Sensing his hostility, she was thrown back on her deepest resources for personal survival, while feeling she had no choice but to hold to her marriage vows. She found ways to occupy herself creatively and maintained an intense inner life of imagination and hope.

After six years of marriage, Elinor found that her health was deteriorating, with the asthma, from which she had always suffered, dramatically worsening. Heathwick Hall, Maldonbury's imposing, ivy-covered mansion-house, had become an echoing prison, full of ghost-sounds and ghost-memories. In particular, Elinor was haunted by the contents of a chamber, screened off by a dusty arras, at the end of a dark passage. This locked room she had opened with one of the keys on a rusty iron ring found, after much searching, in a cobwebbed recess in the kitchen.

The room, on the top floor of the house, contained a coffin-shaped glass case eerily lit by a skylight, which displayed clothes, artefacts and treasures that — as her researches later proved — had belonged to her husband's dead wives. A satin wedding dress, a lorgnette, a shawl of embroidered silk, two cameo brooches and a diamond-studded locket... Elinor gazed at their muted shine then, lifting the glass lid, moved her fingertips over each surface, touching smooth softness and silver chill. She opened the locket and contemplated the beautiful, hopeful face she would come to know as that of her husband's first wife.

Suddenly feeling she was being watched, Elinor turned — to behold her pale, shadowed face in a mirror on the damp wall. Beneath it was a chair on which lay articles that had gone missing from her bedroom in recent months: a handkerchief with scalloped edges, a fan, her long white gloves... In the winter twilight of that room she froze with shock then struggled for breath, as though its dusty air were permeating not only her lungs, but her heart and spirit, too. After escaping from it, Elinor locked the room and put back the keys. Now, the whole house filled her with dread.

Because of her compelling fears regarding Lord Maldonbury's intentions towards her, Elinor chose to stage a disappearance on New Year's Eve, 1899. She began a new life — living for the first year discreetly in Bath, under the name Lavinia Merrivale.

Exactly a year later, her husband vanished from an overnight train between London and Edinburgh on which she also happened to be travelling. Because of the disturbed state of his compartment, foul play was suspected, though not conclusively proved, and he was assumed to be dead. However, his body was never found.

Subsequently, Elinor settled in the Scottish town of Dunkeld with her new husband, Dr Seamus L'Estrange, whom she married — she hoped, not bigamously — at the beginning of 1901. Their union was blessed with a daughter and son.

Thomas Quinn

Thomas was born in 1871 to Maisie and Michael, proprietors of a fish shop on the High Street in Clapham. The young Thomas worked at King's Cross Station as a porter, then as a train conductor, and finally as an attendant on overnight services between London and Edinburgh. He maintained this occupation until his retirement in 1936.

He and his wife Margaret had five children. As a family, they took many rail journeys into the countryside on weekends to have picnics and, as the children grew older, go for long rambles. Their oldest son, David, was to fulfil Thomas's ambition to be a train driver.

Mario Scampare

Born in the village of Buria in Tuscany, Mario was swaddled for an unusually long period as an infant. When a small boy, he was often punished by being confined in a cramped attic where he consoled himself by dressing up in fadedly grand old clothes and, in his imagination, flying or diving into unknown, but benign, worlds beyond the sky and the sea.

As a young man, he trained as a locksmith, and showed a special aptitude for opening locks whose keys were lost or broken. Eventually he gave public performances to demonstrate his amazing gift. During these displays he was placed in handcuffs and bound with chains which were then padlocked: within a matter of minutes he released himself from all constraints. He soon became famous for his exploits as an escape artist, and chose ever more spectacular settings for his feats, such as bridges and waterfalls. Dressed always in flamboyant costumes, he could escape from his bonds while underwater, or dangling from a high tower.

The love of his life was Florence Ellesmere, the British actress. They met early in their lives, when Mario was presenting a performance as an illusionist at a London music-hall. However, after a brief time of happiness together, circumstances parted them. They were never to meet again.

It was soon after his celebrated escape from a frightening array of instruments and devices in the torture chamber of King Ludovico of Bravuria, that Mario was accused of the theft of the Krammstein jewels and arrested in Szenburgh. Though he was, of course, innocent of the theft, the unusual degree of skill, ingenuity and speed involved in the penetration of six locked doors, a vault and a safe, was thought to point indubitably to him.

He was detained in a stronghold on the island of Volnikus for twenty-five years, during which time he composed his memoirs and wrote many volumes of poetry to prevent himself from going mad. Because of the ineffable wound to his pride of his (many times repeated) failure to escape from the island, he found himself unable to write to Florence, who accordingly never learned of his fate.

On leaving the island in the summer of 1907, he travelled to Scotland after learning that Florence had settled in Edinburgh. He arrived too late to be reunited with her as she had died in the spring of that year. However, while paying his respects at Florence's grave, he met one of her friends, Jasper Abbott, who would pass on to him a gift that Jasper himself had given to Florence years before: a small gold-plated and bejewelled clock in the shape of a phoenix. This she had left in trust with her friend some weeks before her unexpected death, in case Mario should ever appear after she had been translated into the beyond — 'Whenever that might be,' she had added, smiling.

Mario was to take this treasure with him through the remaining years of his life. When he died in 1921, the phoenix clock was buried with him. However, because of strange stories which were abroad about a secret treasure, and who knows what else, his grave was re-opened soon after his interment. Thus it was discovered that, along with the clock, Mario himself was missing. Both of them entered into legend. At the time of writing, no further information is available about Mario or the phoenix clock.

Ernest Gaston Watts

Ernest grew up in the village of Grimsworth in East Yorkshire. His mother was Merle Rowland, much admired in her youth for her parian skin and large hazel eyes. His father was the famous chef, Pierre Gaston Quoix, who met his mother at a banquet given by the Earl of Taverner in 1862.

On that occasion, Pierre had created the exquisitely ornate array of delicacies which bedecked the tables. After his duties were completed, he joined the gathering as a guest, and found himself drawn to the baffling intangibility of Merle's beauty. She in turn responded to his almost magical gifts as a transformer of food into art, and the air of opaque strangeness he had about him as one whose origins were in a foreign land.

Their marriage was neither a happy nor an unhappy one — which suited Merle well enough, but was devastating for Pierre. Ernest, their only child, was born a year after their wedding. They travelled with little Ernest to many of the great houses of Britain, where Pierre would design, cook, and oversee sumptuous banquets. Merle particularly loved the sparkle and expensive display of such occasions, and felt herself to be, as indeed she was, in another world.

It was in Scotland that Pierre's life was ended by a tragic accident. He had been invited by his current host to join a shooting party and, while kneeling to tie his shoelace, received a blow to the head from one of the beaters who had fallen back from his position ahead of the shooters. Pierre's last impression before he became unconscious was of a capercaillie flying up noisily and splendidly into the light. He died three days later.

Ernest was four when his father passed away. His mother cared for him as best she could, struggling on alone. But, while her intentions were good, Merle increasingly entered a world of melancholy fantasy, and yearned for the glamorous times when she had mingled with the aristocracy and felt caught up in the resplendent glitter of their lives.

Finally, Merle withdrew from life in general, disappearing even from her own home when despair affected her deeply. Because the past came to seem like a locked room to her, Merle never spoke to Ernest of his father, save on one rather elliptical occasion. She also anglicised her married name, believing she was thus erasing the memory of the husband who had abandoned her by dying.

Ernest was a child who, despite the minimal information granted him — or perhaps because of it — pondered the nature of things constantly, trying hard to fit together a picture of the world. However, his youth was understandably a period of confusion and ordeal. In the course of time, an erratic courage emerged to overthrow his stoic seriousness.

During this phase he became peripatetic, and tasted the variety of life more fully. Eventually he found an odd-shaped niche for himself at New Scotland Yard, where the steady advancement of such a seemingly unprepossessing individual made some eyebrows rise, but mostly escaped notice. The more subtle reaches of crime detection were his domain, and he would often surprise and impress colleagues with his original interpretations of evidence, and his insight into the imponderable reaches of human motivation.

1901 was to prove a year of dramatic change, when Ernest appeared to undergo a loss of confidence in his powers and, indeed, to suffer some form of nervous breakdown. Would he be able to continue in his work for the Yard?

Fortunately, he found help from a surprising source, in the person of his landlady, Mrs Molly Silver — widowed early in her life after three years of marriage, and now managing her establishment independently, while enthusiastically pursuing her passion for cooking. A staunch, outgoing woman, Molly stepped from her habitual breezy cheer to befriend Ernest at this time, and he often held thoughtful conversations with her as she prepared the evening meal or accompanied him for a stroll in the park on Sunday afternoons. There, his personal retinue of ducks and geese still gathered round him beside the lake, despite the lack of his customary whistling to them. Molly would bring a bag of stale bread and together they would feed their flock.

The Saturday evening meal was a feature of life for the paying guests at Grandhaven. It was at one such feast that Ernest was visited by a vivid memory from when he was four: of sitting at a table with a steaming dish at its centre — an example of the cuisine that, as he was soon to discover, had been created by his father. That dish was now before him on Molly's table. On one side of a vast rectangular platter were pieces of chicken in a reddish sauce that Ernest now understood must contain a quantity of red wine; on the other side was a plain beef stew, the thick gravy seasoned by mustard, as he learnt by sampling it. Dividing the two dishes was a line of steamed greens topped with sautéd endive.

That very evening, sitting in Molly's kitchen with a small glass of port to hand, Ernest mentioned the special dish, only to see Molly take an old cookbook down from a shelf and open it at the recipe, *Coq et Boeuf*. The book's author was Pierre Gaston Quoix. There, pictured on the page, was the very dish. This discovery quickly led Ernest to the truth of his paternal parentage, and he began an extensive search into the facts of his father's life. Subsequently, he incorporated his father's middle name into his own name.

Ernest and Molly married in 1902. Ernest filled out considerably under Molly's ardent culinary influence, and their companionship both deepened and mellowed over the years.

Only one eccentricity of Ernest's persisted in bemusing Molly, which was his firm rule that Mrs Beeton's celebrated book on household management not be kept at Grandhaven, nor any of its many recipes used by her.

The couple lived to enjoy a ripe old age — during which they had, respectively, many heinous unspeakable crimes solved, and many wondrously enticing and delectable dinners cooked, to look back upon.

Claire Westwood

Born Claire Framer, in 1894. Her early childhood was spent in London, but at the age of six she was taken by her mother to live in Kilrush, on the west coast of Ireland. Claire loved music and, from the age of eighteen, gave piano lessons, following in the steps of her mother. In 1920, she married Gerald Mulhearn, a farmer, and in their life together they raised four children.

Helen Westwood

Born in 1864, Helen grew up in Liskeard, Cornwall. Her father, William Petherell, was a chemist, and her mother, Vanessa, a dressmaker. She met George Framer when he visited the town on holiday in 1892. They married and she moved to London where he had a business making and selling hats. Their daughter Claire was born two years later.

Following her escape from the tyrannous Framer in the last week of 1900, Helen journeyed with her daughter to Scotland, bound for a steamboat to Ireland. However, they were delayed when Claire became seriously ill, and stayed for some weeks in Ayr. Upon her recovery, Helen took Claire to the sacred island of Iona to offer thanksgiving.

While there she met Fergus McVeigh, who had sailed from Ireland with a party on an archeological expedition to the western islands of Scotland in the summer of 1900. However, Fergus had chosen to leave the party so as to stay longer on Iona and continue his study of its archeological remains.

In February, 1901, Helen and Claire Westwood sailed with Fergus McVeigh for Ireland then crossed to the west to settle in his homeplace, Kilrush, situated by the Shannon estuary. Helen found employment as a piano teacher. She and Claire lived within sight of the ancient monastic settlement on Scattery Island, and often were rowed there on Saturday afternoons by Fergus McVeigh in his small boat with its sky-blue sail.

Charlotte Winter

Born in Yorkshire in 1869. She was raised by her aunts, Mary and Minnie Bridmore, from the age of five, after the death of her mother, Lucy Winter. Lucy had worked as a governess at Crockley Castle, seat of the Fortesque family, until five months before Charlotte's birth. (Lord Vivian Fortesque had financially supported Lucy after her dismissal, but covertly — never acknowledging Charlotte as his daughter.)

At a midsummer ball at Larches, the home of Mr and Mrs Greystoke, the twenty-year-old Charlotte had met Robert Childers and fallen in love with him. However, his insistence on keeping their friendship secret, combined with the pressing nature of his attentions, alerted her to the ambivalent nature of his interest in her. Accordingly, she departed for a position as a governess at Vaneston Towers in Sussex without informing him, and instructing her fond aunts to withhold from him the details of her new location.

In the following years, when beset by moments of regret, Charlotte consoled herself with the knowledge that her painful isolation and hard-won independence were a refuge from, and bastian against, the fate of being actively unloved. While, as a governess, she had sometimes felt joy in the growth in mind and character of her young charges, Charlotte found her employers to be often glacially indifferent, or spitefully demanding people. Thus, over the years, her moods tended to shuttle between hope and a terminal weariness.

However, she was to experience something like comic exasperation, mixed with an almost eerie detachment, in her final posting with Lord and Lady McRossiter of Rumbervie Castle at Rossvale in Midlothian, and Turrets in Kensington, London. During that time, despite a large quotient of diverting and even bizarre occurrences, a feeling that life could no longer surprise her settled into her bones.

This feeling, it seemed to Charlotte's better self, was the worst enemy of all. However, what could she do but go on according to her lights, as she had always done? To struggle, endure, and be silent (except for the occasional overly incisive word that somehow escaped from her lips) — this was the pact she made with herself. She was too humble to allow herself to judge that life was disappointing, yet ... it was difficult to find acceptance within herself, or rest in a sense of fulfilment because of what she had given to others.

It was at Waverley Station, on the first day of 1901, that Charlotte found the turning point she was — despite inner avowals to the contrary — awaiting. But first, the fierce blow from Lord McRossiter that left her reeling. His rage had been fuelled by a night on whisky, and some vicious rumours regarding his wife — all of which were indeed true. And he had seemed intent on holding the three women present — Anne Morgan and herself as well as Lady McRossiter — to ransom for his humiliation.

Because of what Charlotte ever afterwards thought of as 'The Upheaval', Lady McRossiter was to decide to exile herself to Venice for the rest of her life; Lord McRossiter — facing imminent collapse of body and mind, and still perversely lusting after herself — was to ask her forgiveness and immediately propose marriage (how she had enjoyed saying 'No!' before drawing her next breath); and she was to meet Alasdair Lockhart, whom she married.

In later years, Charlotte found herself possessed of the luxury of ample time to pursue the passionate interest in birds she had acquired soon after that event. She became a painter of birds, creating convincing depictions of wren and jackdaw, sparrow and barn owl, robin and lark. After travels abroad with her husband, she was able to add more exotic examples of bird life to her repertoire.

One of her gifts was for stillness, so Alasdair insisted — though Charlotte never forgot to breathe as she sat with her hand skating slowly over the page, and her eyes barely moving as they focused on a parrot's rainbowed presence among eucalyptus leaves, or contemplated the drop of water growing on the end of a heron's beak, concentrating the day's light within it before dropping to seed bronze-and-gold rings on the surface of a radiant grey lake.

THE MASKED BALL

'The Masked Ball'

by Rosa Morland

The last night of the nineteenth century had arrived. Lady Cynthia Sommerton had long since decided that *this* New Year's Eve ball would be a masked one, and now stood welcoming her guests. Standing at the top of the steps leading to the chandeliered ballroom, she felt an intoxicating lightness, as if her priceless Venetian mask had removed decades from her age.

When Sarah Ormond entered the great doorway of Bellingham Hall, accompanied by her aunt, Mrs Diana Greville, she was recognised at once despite her dainty mask fringed with black lace, and greeted warmly. 'Destined for the life of a governess, I don't doubt,' thought Lady Cynthia. 'A sweet but very retiring young lady... indeed, not so young any more. I believe she's twenty-three.'

Soon Sarah was chatting with her friend Emily then was taken for a spinning waltz around the ballroom floor by her favourite cousin, Will, who was on his best behaviour, though still his usual exuberant self. The mask was a help with her social awkwardness, and Sarah felt quite taken out of herself for a time. There was much to enjoy — the sparkling atmosphere, the butterfly-bright gowns and abundant smiles — yet before long she found herself sitting by a large potted fern in a corner of the ballroom, thinking her own thoughts and watching the ecstatic whirl of dancing couples from a distance.

Her first glimpse of him was brief, dream-like — the man in the floor-length black cape standing outside the open doors of the ballroom, seemingly taking in the whole scene through the eye-holes in his narrow mask, so tight it seemed moulded onto his face. There was a flash of crimson as he turned away suddenly; within two minutes he was back at the same spot without his cape, his evening clothes in a slightly different style from those worn by the other male guests. When he entered and walked slowly down the left side of the ballroom, she noticed his severe limp and curved posture. It was as though the sense of ambivalence about him extended even to his height — he might once have been quite a tall man.

Framed by long, but sparse, jet-black hair, his ashen face was lopsided too. Later, when Sarah heard him talking behind her at the supper table — why was he hovering there for so long? — she surmised he might have had a stroke, for he spoke with some difficulty. She went on eating her cress sandwich with the odd feeling she'd heard his voice before — but that was impossible. Besides, he had a foreign accent; Sarah had never travelled beyond her home in Fawnfield, a place to which foreigners rarely came.

When, towards midnight, she again sat dreaming under the umbrella-like fern, Sarah became aware that the unknown man had his eyes fixed upon her — they were an intensely pale blue, startling inside his black mask. She felt shock at first, then... fascination, perhaps? Or pity? Whatever the emotion might be, it was morbid! Briskly she took herself off to the card-tables to survey the wily manoeuvres of her aunt Diana, seated among her cronies at one table, while Squire Fothergill engaged in verbal jousting with other red-faced hearties at another.

Some of the conversation she caught was about *him*. He'd arrived three months earlier... from Germany — or was it Hungary? Or Romania, perhaps? Hard to tell from the accent, opined Major Garth Blunt, who had lived in many places abroad and knew about such things. Oh, but a well-resourced gentleman! Already he had restored the interior of the old castle; much talk circulated about the sumptuous banquets held there. He was a keen horseman — and a great one for riding to hounds. In fact, there was a hunt planned for next week. Hunting was the passion, it was said, that had brought the Count to this place.

Sarah needed fresh air... On the balcony, she fluttered her ivory fan while breathing in the scent of camellias. She felt as if that fragrance, elusive yet enveloping, were stroking her skin, reaching into her very soul. Watching the full moon — just now partly masked by a reef of dark cloud — she was suddenly aware of cigar smoke drifting towards her in the slight breeze. She turned quickly. The Count bowed to her.

'A pleazant evfning, Madmwazell! May I azk ivf you havf one danz levft vfrei?'

'Alas, I have injured my leg,' said Sarah, uttering the first thought that came to her.

'Ahg, thet makz tu ovf uz!'

He laughed bitterly then bowed again and, after throwing his cigar into the camellia bush, limped inside.

Sarah took a deep, deep breath to calm herself, but unfortunately some smoke still lingered in the air around her. It entered her throat. She felt herself cough then gasp. One of her attacks was starting! Fearing a sudden collapse, she looked wildly round, turned on her heel and rushed back through the open French windows. Chandelier flames exploding... a crash... total blackness.

Next thing, all her cousins were clustered about her, attending her on the sofa. Beyond them, Sarah thought she saw a fleeting shadow, a grey eminence — like the spectre of her own death, it seemed to her at that moment. But she recovered before long, her mood brightening again as her cousin Will helped her into

Lady Cynthia's carriage which would take her and Aunt Diana home.

Such a strange man, she thought afterwards. And dangerous? Some said so. She found him sad. It was frequently whispered by the folk of Fawnfield that he kept a mistress locked up in a tower of the castle. Another story — which would be truly frightening if it were not so absurd! — claimed that he was given to drinking the blood of slain animals, and always had a flask of fresh blood by him. Then it was widely held, (though of course quite impossible to believe), that he...

Indeed, it was because so many rumours abounded that her aunt decided Sarah must refuse the invitation to ride to hounds, sent by the Count the next day — despite the fact that he was fabulously rich, and notable personages from miles around would be there... ('How fascinating it would be to observe them all!' Sarah had thought.) Misreading her preoccupied smile, Aunt Diana said, 'We're quiet people who must mind our p's and q's,' adding, with her calmly resigned smile, 'Besides, my dear, you're so very fragile'. But Sarah found she had no regrets, as she would much prefer to stay indoors and continue the novel she was writing.

The novel concerned... well, yes, it did deal with her own fantasies about her future life to some extent. It was about a young governess, Sophie Oliphant:

After taking an advertised position, Sophie finds herself trapped on a vast, isolated estate, in charge of two unruly children, Quentin and Lillian. Desolation! — but she meets the situation with courage. The children's widowed father, Sir Desmond Carstairs, is abroad when she arrives — due to return in a month's time. But he does not appear on the day he is expected, nor during the week following.

The whole household at Raventhorpe waits with increasing anxiety when no word from the Master comes. What should she do? The housekeeper, Mrs Pollard, is taken aback by Sophie's plan to ride to the nearest town then take a coach to the port where her employer was due to arrive ten days ago. Perhaps the Master has been waylaid by rowdies after disembarking from his ship — or has met with some other form of foul play? At least if she makes enquiries she can find out if he actually arrived... After demurring, Mrs Pollard eventually agrees that Sophie may set out on the journey.

On reaching the port town, whom should she meet but an old school friend, Edwina Skewton. They embrace warmly, and Edwina is able to tell Sophie of the docking of The Free Spirit *twelve days ago. 'It's a rough town,' she warns her, 'but if you are bent on finding this man, you must go to the inn called* The Anchor and Feather.' *Sophie sets out for it immediately.*

What forces could Sarah bring into play now? She chewed the end of her pen then decided to take a cup of tea while she thought about the matter. Soon after, her aunt came in with the latest gossip. A new doctor was coming to town. Little was known about him, but... Returning to her small table, Sarah found herself writing him into her novel.

Her heroine has twisted her ankle while searching for more information about the arrival of The Free Spirit, *having tripped on one of the cobblestones in a lane leading down to the docks. A kindly woman assists Sophie to her modest home nearby, and calls for Dr Wetherall. When he enters the parlour where she is lying on the sofa, Sophie is startled by his gentle brown eyes and composed face. He has chestnut hair, and looks to be about twenty-eight.*

How Sarah was to laugh at herself a few weeks later when Dr Granger arrived in Fawnfield. He was a bluff yet courteous middle-aged man whose complexion suggested he might be rather too fond of port. Ah well! However, at the dinner given by Squire Fothergill to welcome him to Fawnfield, Dr Granger spoke of the imminent arrival of his son, Frank, now making his way home from Vienna.

It happened that on the day before he was due to arrive, Sarah was walking along a lane shaded by overarching ash and beech trees. Looking up to follow the flight of a warbler, she became aware of a figure riding towards her, blocking the way through. Was it Frank Granger, already — come a day early? But no — she soon saw that it was the Count approaching her, on a huge black steed. She controlled her trepidation and nerved herself for the inevitable encounter.

In a few minutes he was looming above her, and removed his hat with a flourish.

'A vfyn day, Miz Zarah!'

'Truly it is, Count.'

Suddenly, the scent of honeysuckle overwhelmed her with an almost hypnotic heaviness. He stayed looking at her intently, with his strange Continental silence, as if he were contemplating sweeping her up on his horse and riding away. Oh, she must not give in to an attack of breathlessness now — she would be helpless! Up close to him she saw that his face, lit by a beam of cruelly sharp sunlight, was seamed with scars — as if it had been patched together. Again she shrank from him, while seeking to remain mistress of the situation.

At that very moment, she heard the distant sound of a carriage on the main road — could it be, Frank was really coming early? But she must not rely on being rescued. Sarah gathered her wits, struggling to breathe evenly.

'Farewell, Count, I must hurry on to deliver these cakes to the Misses Fairfax.'

Then she had walked straight ahead, manoeuvring herself gracefully past the sweating steed, which she knew would be unable to turn in the lane...

Whether or not Frank Granger had come early, Sarah did not find out until the following week — he had not. In the meantime, she had been too busy writing her novel to listen to gossip about the doings in Fawnfield. And she was already writing Frank into the novel so that, should he prove a disappointment in real life — which she was quite prepared for — she would have the company of the fictional Frank, known as Edward Grey.

In the event, Frank was not a disappointment. Tall, but not too tall, with chestnut hair and a sensitive face, he was a charming and intelligent companion when she and her aunt went to dinner at his father's house. Frank was to be a physician himself, and had been travelling widely — visiting places such as Paris, Antwerp, Venice and Prague — before returning to complete his studies in London.

Sometimes, on the walks Sarah would take with Frank later on in their acquaintance, she would glimpse the castle towers in the distance and feel her breath sucked away. On such occasions, Sarah thought how fortunate she was to have a medical student as a friend. But it was for himself she appreciated him — a good-hearted, generous man, open as a book, who yet carried the flavour of unknown places about him.

Would they one day marry? Sarah did not know if it was meant to be, though Frank was often in her thoughts. In the meantime, there was her novel. She found herself entranced by her new hero, Edward. But she must not become too involved with him — life was, after all, more important than novels! And there were moments, out walking with Frank, when a feeling — quite odd, but rather wonderful — crept over her, as if she were standing beneath a tree full of fluttering doves. Often, at such times, Frank himself became strangely, deeply, quiet — which was a little unnerving perhaps, but most interesting.

Today there was a fire burning in the hearth. Although spring was on its way, it cheered her to have a small jewel-like blaze while she was writing. And, as usual, there was a damask rose in the alabaster vase on her writing-table. Outside, the light was growing brighter — about mid-morning, she supposed.

Her gaze drifted to the branches of the birch and elm trees framed by her window. Sarah thought she saw a vividly coloured parrot perch on a branch of the linden tree beyond them — only to fly quickly away. But no doubt this was an illusion, as she did not know how such an exotic bird could visit a place such as Fawnfield. However, that need not prevent her from putting the bird into her novel.

Accordingly, her head bent over the page, she found herself relating that her heroine receives a mysterious gift: a resplendent macaw — it would be scarlet and blue and gold, Sarah decided. It is found outside the front door one morning — just imagine! — in an ornate gold cage, like a miniature palace.

Once again oblivious of her surroundings, Sarah wrote on, her slightly freckled hand reaching from time to time to dip her pen into the ebony inkwell — an old favourite of hers, with its engraved depiction of a wide-winged phoenix above its burning nest.

But look at the hour! — she must finish this chapter before Frank called in with the book he had promised to lend her. Oh, what was its title? And the author's name? Dear me, did it start with an 'A' , or a 'B' perhaps, or 'C' or 'D' — maybe even an 'E'? Well, no matter! The sun had reached its modest height over the village of Fawnfield as Sarah, in the grip of a waking dream, wrote on and on and on.

About the Author

DIANE FAHEY lives in the Victorian coastal town of Barwon Heads — the setting of her recent poetry collection, *Sea Wall and River Light*. Her seven other collections variously engage with Greek myths, fairytales, visual art, nature writing, and autobiographical themes.

Diane has published and read her poems internationally, and her poetry has appeared in over 60 anthologies. She has received a number of poetry awards, including the Mattara Poetry Prize, the Wesley Michel Wright Poetry Prize, the Judith Wright Prize, and the John Shaw Neilson Poetry Prize, as well as a Felix Meyer Scholarship from the University of Melbourne to research Greek mythology in Greece.

She has been awarded writer's fellowships and grants from Arts SA and Arts Victoria, and from the Australia Council — from which she also received support for writer's residencies in Venice, at the Tyrone Guthrie Centre in Ireland, and at the University of Adelaide. Other residencies have been at Hawthornden International Writers' Centre, Scotland, and at Varuna — The Writers' House, in the Blue Mountains.

She holds the degrees of BA and MA in Literature, and a PhD in Creative Writing for her study 'Places and Spaces of the Writing Life'.

An interview with Diane Fahey can be found in *Thylazine* No. 9 – www.thylazine.org.

Comments on Diane Fahey's Poetry

With the publication of her first volume of poetry, *Voices from the Honeycomb*, Diane Fahey should be immediately established among poets of solid reputation. These poems are perceptive, moving and accomplished: the book reads like a third or fourth volume.

— Chris Wallace-Crabbe, *National Times*

Metamorphoses, the title of Diane Fahey's recent book of poetry, is particularly apt. Not only do many of the characters in the stories she uses undergo transformation, the myths themselves change in shape as their underlying values are exposed and constructed by Fahey. ... The changes which are effected in *Metamorphoses* are, in the end, changes in consciousness; they lead to an apprehension of the recurring cycles of life and death, intimacy and betrayal, repression and renascence.

— Meg Tasker, *Australian Women's Book Review*

Diane Fahey's *Turning the Hourglass* observes the balanced contours of its title. This is a most shapely and carefully constructed volume. In five parts, it tells of a necessary journey to freedom and self-discovery. ... A reserve and dignity restrain Fahey from presenting a purely confessional account of the facts inspiring the poems. Many poems bear a date and name a place, but much else is left to conjecture. Metaphors of light and darkness convey other truths.

— Heather Cam, *Sydney Morning Herald*

Like her 'Dragonfly', Fahey has always been a 'cartographer of translucent maps'. The best poems in all her books are full of light and effects of light and of sound, the presence and resonance of water; transparency; flight; growth and change and time. In *Mayflies in Amber* there is a spinning-out of space and silence, in structures that are sparer, plainer, tighter for the most part, in this book: distichs and tercets with hardly a long line anywhere.

— Beverley Farmer, *Voices*

Fahey writes with a confident maturity that understates rather than flaunts itself. Her work in *The Body in Time* has an impressive, uncompromising integrity. It is so free of egotistical schedules and so quietly accomplished that it shows us that Diane Fahey is a poet who has a great amount to teach.

— Judith Beveridge, *Cordite*

Her poetry is so undemonstrative, that few people will be aware that Diane Fahey is now one of our major poets. It is difficult to characterise her voice in this new collection — 'quiet assurance' is the obvious phrase that comes to mind, but it fails to capture the strength, and the determination of her poetic approach. Her honesty is most apparent when she turns her gaze upon herself — always the test of a good poet — and she does that repeatedly in this collection. ... Fahey brings the same moral rigour to the profession of poetry as she does to laying bare of her feelings.

— Ivor Indyk on *The Body in Time*, in *Heat*

Fahey's style is expansive and inventive. She runs off variations on the themes of myth with ease and fluency, rewriting them to fit our own cultural and personal psychologies. She also deals up witty changes on the old stories to satirise the present. ... Fahey's volume is clever poetry, carrying its civilisation lightly, and chatting to us in entertaining tongues...

— Julian Croft on *Listening to a Far Sea*, in *Ulitarra*

In *The Sixth Swan* ... readers will detect nothing of the author's private life. They will however, form a strong sense of her personality: introspective, sardonic, drawn to the mystical, and with a love of language for its own sake. ... Many of the poems ... are impressive feats of social observation or pure imagination.

— Geoff Page, *Australian Book Review*

Sea Wall and River Light is a collection of seventy fourteen-line poems set in and around Barwon Heads in Victoria. ... The poems seem drawn gently out of the life of the place – they carry the energy of it within them. ... [The poet] watches and records simple events with a warmth and a gravity that actually inspires the reader to observe their own places in a similar spirit. Fahey is intensely aware of what she is doing with language, and confident within its domain. ... Her way with meter and the sound of words is breathtakingly adept.

— Andy Jackson, *Cordite*

Diane Fahey is a wide-ranging accomplished poet, highly deserving of her growing international reputation.

— Katherine Gallagher, *Poetry Review*